A special dedication goes, Alison, of Alison';
Upon Hull, United Kingdom for all their supp
in Hull.

And another special thanks to the good people of Hull and the region of East
Yorkshire for their support in making the Scallywag book series so successful
and official best sellers.

You are about to enter the weird and wonderful world of the Celebrity Lookalike.

As a Rod Stewart Lookalike I worked with the following celebrity lookalikes.

Queen Elizabeth II
Elvis.
The Polish Pope.
Alvin Stardust.
Clint Eastwood as Dirty Harry.
The gorgeous and sexy Debbie Harry.
Humphrey Bogart.
Cary Grant.
Albert Steptoe
And many many others. It was the late 1970's and early 1980's. It was a time of party, fun, loads of free alcohol and some of the most beautiful and wealthy girls on tap. I say without hesitation, "I filled my boots."

I was Rod Stewart's Double.
The Sordid Confessions of a Rod Stewart lookalike
(A true story)
By

Terry Cox

Scallywag Books
A division of:

NEXT STOP
LAX

Work Building, 7083 Hollywood Blvd. Hollywood, CA, 90028.
Contact us: + 1 323 798 5102   Email: info@nextstoplax.com

Copyright © 2017 Andrew Newton Lee (51%) and Terry Cox (49%) as agreed.
First published in Great Britain in 2017 by Scallywag Books.
Email: scallywagbooks@gmail.com

Andrew Newton Lee/Terry Cox have asserted their rights to be identified as the
author
of this work under the Copyright, Designs and Patents Act
1988.

A CIP catalogue record for this book is
available from the British Library
ISBN: 978-0-9935547-2-8
Published by: Scallywag Books. Book Packagers and Publishers London and
Hull. Phone UK 07539732661 or 07732215251

Printed in The People Republic of China

Other Scallywag Books:

Hessle Road Scallywags (official comedy best seller)
Hessle Road Scallywags 2 – A Brief Encounter in Hull
Hessle Road Scallywags 3- The Return to the Street of misfits
Salty Sea Stories by Terry Cox
Dustbingate
Pizza Wars
The Night Shift
Silent Backlash – now unavailable.

Other publications:
Mohsen's Rush.
The Highest Emissary
Dustbingate – The Film Script

All the above are also available on Amazon Kindle.
Out soon in paperback: 2018
by Ian Newton and Terry Cox
Hessle Road Scallywags 4 - The Search for Christmas.

Cover and illustrations by Ray Allan. www.idrawanyface.com
E mail: Ray@idrawanyface.com
Tel: 0797781104

Printed by courtesy of The Daily Star

Two of my Elvis Lookalike colleagues, as you can see just a little over weight.

Her Majesty the "Queen" (Lookalike) arrives for a good old booze up at a Lookalike party with Parker, her trusty chauffeur, come Butler, come gardener, come body guard and general "Royal" house hold dog's body.

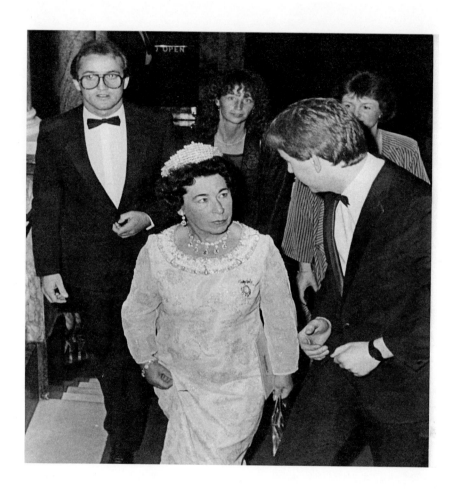

Her "Majesty" being chatted up by one of the local peasants.
The Queen explaining that the Duke of Edinburgh couldn't
make it because of his severe hemorrhoids and athlete's foot.

Her "Majesty" the Queen leaves the booze up early as she finds out it is not a free bar. Here Her "Majesty" waves to the great unwashed and smelly who have been waiting for hours outside freezing their bollocks off in the freezing cold to pay homage.

Picture and story courtesy of Hull Daily Mail (1981)

Pop fans mob Rod Stewart Double

SNAP: Look-alike Terry

EVERY picture tells a story... and Yorkshire lass Gloria Subria had every reason to believe the guy chatting her up was superstar Rod Stewart. But the lad who was to sweep her off her feet was super star lookalike Terry Cox. He has been signed up by a top London based Lookalike agency to work on TV commercials.

Terry, 27, a merchant seaman has been mistaken for Rod Stewart all over the world. Once in Holland, he won a fancy dress contest without even entering it. Terry was in a merchant seaman's social club in Amsterdam while the contest was being held. He only popped in to find one of his mates and ended up winning the contest. Last year in Paris Airport he was mobbed as he tried to make his way through customs.

Terry of Hazel Road, Hull, Yorkshire, said: "It was quite frightening really, I didn't think I was going to get out alive. It's happened a few times when travelling abroad.

"When I go to foreign ports, I am always being mobbed by flocks of girls. I suppose it's one of the advantages of looking like Rod, but my girlfriend Gloria doesn't agree, and she gets a bit jealous I suppose."

Terry said:

"Sometimes I get a bit fed up with girls and people pestering me for autographs and photos. One time in Stockholm, I got scared out of my wits, as I had this horde of Swedish school girls chasing through the streets and I got trapped in this shop, and the police had to rescue me. I lost my shirt and almost my jeans and I came out covered in lipstick, cuts and bruises. It scared me to death I can tell you"

A MESSAGE TO ALL THOSE POST WAR CHILDREN OUT THERE FROM SCALLYWAG BOOKS.

Scallywag books was formed in 2013 by two friends Ian Achmed and Terry Cox. Ian Achmed was a senior mental health professional and Terry Cox was a merchant navy deck officer. Both are now retired. What bonded these two people together was that they grew up together, and both struggled their way out of the poverty of the under-class post-war, bombed-out slums of Hull's Hessle Road area in the United Kingdom. They had been lifelong street buddies and school friends. But in 1969 after leaving school at fifteen years old, they would go their separate ways, and take very separate roads in life, and never the twain shall meet, as they say. After 47 years and careers that had taken both around the world, they bumped into each other and exchanged memories of their now, long gone childhood days.

If there was one subject that arose more than any during that conversation, it was that they rarely laughed anymore, they never watched TV, read newspapers, or read books. It seemed their time had gone, and the world they came from which had moulded them had been consigned to the dustbin of history.

And that gave them idea. They wondered how many millions more were like them? Yearning to laugh again at the bawdy humour of Steptoe and Son, On The Buses, Rising Damp and many other comedy greats. So together, you might say, they devised a social experiment. They would write a no-holds barred comedy book about their time growing up as children, and the fun and mischief they got up on those hard post-war streets of the 1950s.

And the results were astounding. With only local publicity, the first book was published in February 2013 and within three weeks the publisher was notified by Neilsen's book ratings agency that this first offering, Hessle Road Scallywags, had entered the official best seller listings. More comedy books followed and four years later all still proudly occupy the shelves of Waterstones and WH Smith and are regular sellers.

The results showed, that indeed there was a neglected audience out there that yearned to laugh again, that yearned for memories of their youth.

So we hope you enjoy our latest "Scallywag" comedy adventure, as Terry Cox puts pen to paper and describes his time as Rod Stewart's double, working for a lookalike agency in the heady days of the1970s, in between trips to sea.

THIS IS FOR THE FORGOTTEN AND NEGLECTED GENERATION OF POST-WAR BRITAIN. OUR GENERATION.

INTRODUCTION
(And just how the hell did I get talked into writing this book?)

Just a small word of warning before we begin. This book does contain what might be described as bad language and some sexually explicit narrative. So if you are easily offended, this book might not be to your delicate sensibilities and taste. Otherwise if you do decide to purchase my literary masterpiece, which is already being compared to Shakespeare and Steptoe and Son in some circles, then I hope you will enjoy it.

A further word from the author Terry Cox.

I don't know how I got talked into writing this book, but I have this very dodgy mate who I grew up with and whose name I won't mention, as he is not well liked by some of the great and so-called 'good' of the city of Hull in the UK. In fact the very mention of his name makes a lot of people in Hull nervous, especially politicians. Even mice have been known to start jumping on mouse traps at the sound of his name.

So let's plod on. Anyway, one day I'm in pub with this dodgy mate and we are downing a few pints and reminiscing about the old days. As usual I seem to be the one getting the beer in, as every time it's his turn to put his hand in his pocket he bolts to the bog. I'm not saying my mate is greedy and selfish but he could peel a banana in his pocket and leave you to slip on peel. He's so tight he squeaks when he walks. I don't know why I put up with him really, but he's an old mate and I suppose I feel sorry for the rich Tory-voting bastard. I mean, it must be really hard work driving that brand new Land Rover, and his Audi and the new Jaguar he never uses that sit in his triple door garage.

And you can guarantee when he arranges to meet you in a pub he's always arrives late so you get to the bar first. He's a bit like the Queen, he never carries cash. And God forbid, if he ever gets to the pub first, he will just loiter around the bar waiting until I get there, order the drinks and then suddenly - shock and horror - he will pat himself down like he's searching for something. And surprise, surprise, what do you know? You guessed it, he's left his wallet and money belt at home. I think the last time I saw him get paper money out, it was one of those big white five pound notes. Yes, it's real hard work to get this dodgy mate to pay for anything. I gave up long ago arguing with him because of his 'heart trouble', and just surrender to the inevitable and dip my hand in my pocket. As I pass over my money to the barman my dodgy mate will quickly jump in, and usually quips with this London spiv smile, "Stick a bag of large peanuts on that will ya' barman."

I am giving you taste of my dodgy mate because I want to give my side of the story, and sort of prepare my defence, as I have a feeling this book will likely end up with me being splashed all over the Sunday newspapers, with my mate, likely be nowhere to be seen, particularly after Rod Stewart sues me.

Now my mate has a bob or two stashed under his mattress, and avoiding getting his round in ensures that I

will likely stay poor while he will die rich. I don't know really why I put up with his tight-fisted ways, but he's an old mate and so I suppose you just do.
So anyway, let's plod on and see how this pans out.

Just to remind you, we are still in the pub. As we are talking and generally putting the world to rights, suddenly my mate has this brain storm and mentions about the time I worked as a Rod Stewart lookalike on and off in between sea trips for this London-based agency in the 1970s and 1980s.
Well my mate might be dodgy, but he does have this curious knack of making money out of the most bizarre schemes - a lot of money in fact - and he also has business contacts all over the place. This mate is always up to something dodgy. Anyway, we are both sat at the bar, and we are laughing about all these funny stories I am telling about my time as a Rod Stewart lookalike. Suddenly my mate has this eureka moment, and his eyes flash open like a mad man, and I'm sure I see pound signs rolling around like a cash register.
"That's it!" he suddenly shouts aloud and makes me jump.
"What is?" I ask, and he turns to me, with eyes still glaring, with a big smile of Biblical revelation spreading across his face.
"Why don't you write a book about it!" he says at me all loud and wide-eyed, "Of course, why didn't I think about it before?" he says aloud, "I have this mate who is publisher, I'll have word."
"What are you on about?" I snap at him. "A book about what, daft lad?"
"About your time as a Rod Stewart lookalike," he says looking hard at me. "I don't think it's been done before."

As I said, the thing about my mate is that he does have some funny, off-the-wall ideas, but he always makes money, lots of money in fact. And he had me thinking now. "Are you serious?" I asked back curiously.

"Why not?" he grins, "It's a bloody good story, and original. There's no originality anywhere these days."

But as always with this dodgy mate, he always has an angle, and I have a feeling one big, BUT, is coming. So my mate duly pitches the small print.

"But if I get you into print, then I want half the royalties," he adds, and he holds out his hand and we shake on it.

"It's a deal," I say, and I duly count my fingers after the handshake. None of them are missing and my wallet is still in my back pocket.

So the next day my mate wastes no time, rushing into my house without knocking, like a man on a mission, and spilling out all the patter of a Cockney second hand car salesman.

"Just a minute," I said indignantly, "Do you mind knocking. For all you know I could be doggying our lass over the kitchen table."

My mate just laughs, "You should be so lucky. They don't make Viagra in that strength."

"I don't know, I have me moments. So just bloody knock next time."

Having put my foot down, I can see he has brought this contract round, almost with the ink still wet and about the length of Tolstoy's War and Peace. I think I would have had less trouble understanding the Magna Carter.

"Who drew this up then,?" I ask "Del Boy?" Anyway I sort of skim read it, but gave up after a couple of pages. It might have well have been in Chinese for all the legal jargon in it. I groaned, and decided to take my life in my hands and signed it. I had a feeling I knew what Dr Faustus felt like after selling his soul to the Devil. I sort of signed, and resigned myself to my fate. After all, what have I got to lose? And my mate assures me we can make a killing.

"You just listen to me my old son," says my mate with this evil glint in his eye. "And you won't go far wrong."

Now where have I heard that one before, I think to myself? And I remembered as two scruffy, dirt poor under-class kids, down Hessle Road in Hull in the post war bombed out slums of the 1960s, me and this mate grew up inseparable as friends. Even then we always had some angle for making a few bob. It didn't always end well as I remember, and sometimes we caused more mayhem than any money we made. Then a thought occurred to me. "Just a minute," I said to my dodgy mate, "What if Rod Stewart sues me?"

My mate looked at me and groaned. "There ya' go already Tez, with your negative vibes. You've got to think positive mate."

"Yeah, but it's alright for you," I said. "But it's my moniker on the front cover?"

My mates shakes his head, "Look will ya' stop worrying and let your Uncle Ian take care of everything."

"But what if Rod Stewart does sue me?" I said back at him again.

"It's got nothing to do with Rod Stewart has it?" my mate assures me. "I mean it's about your time as a Rod Stewart lookalike. In fact, imitation is the highest form of flattery as they say. Rod Stewart will probably love it, and I hear he's a very down to earth guy. He's not the type that sues anyway. He'll probably just send around two big Scottish blokes to break your legs and call it quits."

"Well that's reassuring, but what if he does sue me?" I said again.

"What's he gonna sue ya' for?" my dodgy mate says with a mocking laugh, "You haven't got a penny to scratch your arse with. You only sue people who have money."

"A good point," I conceded.

My mate greedily rubs his hands together and lets out a suspicious evil smile, "Get the beer out then ya' greedy bastard, and we'll drink on it," he says and proceeds to plonk himself down on my living room couch like he owns the place.

And so with a big troubled sigh at what I was getting myself into, I liberated a couple of cans of lager out the fridge and he downs a can in one without taking a breath, and looks at me expectantly. I roll my eyes, as protest is pointless with my mate, and I get him another beer. But I did have other worries about this book caper.

"But what about my Matchbox toy car collection?" I ask him. "That's worth a bob or two. I'll blame you if Rod Stewart sues me for it."

"I can guarantee you that Rod Stewart won't sue you for your toy Matchbox car collection," says my mate. "He's got a garage full of the real McCoy."

And so my dodgy mate talked me into it. "And don't forget, you're luckier than most," he tells me.

"How do you work that one out," I say to him.

"You've got me for a mate," he answers with this serious face.

And that's supposed to reassure me?

"And," says my mate carrying on regardless, "if Rod Stewart does sue you, I'm right behind you and I'll always visit you in prison, or the hospital." My mate starts laughing. "Just joking, Tez. By the way have you got any pictures of you as this Rod Stewart lookalike?"

"Not many. The third wife ripped up the lot after she fleeced me dry. You know what women can be like."

"The third wife!" my mate gasped, "Just how many wives have you had?"

I tried to shrug my shoulders innocently, "Two or three."

"Two or three? You're not a Mormon are you? You mean you lost count? So which is it, two or three?"

I knew I was going to have trouble explaining this, "Three and half really."

"Just a minute," says my mate issuing a long breath, "How can you have three and a half wives?"

"Well I was getting married to number four," I answered awkwardly, "and like, she err, she didn't turn up."

"Bloody hell," my mate swooned. "Three and half wives. What's wrong with you? No wonder you're broke."

"We just weren't compatible that's all. I'm like on a higher plane, more spiritual and artistic. They just didn't understand my needs for existential thought and challenge and that I was a free spirit."

"For fuck sake, talk English!"

"They caught me banging other birds," I conceded sheepishly, and shrugged my shoulders.

My mate groaned and rolled his eyes skywards. "Yeah, that sounds more like it."

"Alright," I snapped back, "don't rub it in."

"But you must have some photos left?" my mate blurted back again.

"I might have some gathering dust, why?"

"Well dig them out, I've got an idea for the front cover and I've already got some magazines interested in running a story and get this," he says with his voice rising in childlike glee, "I might be able to get you on that Loose Women show!"

I was getting a bit nervy now, "How ya' going to manage that?"

"My son Andy, knows Denise Welsh real well. She stays at his pad in LA all the time. And she's on Loose Women."

"Oh I don't know about that," I say with a note of dread.

"There you go again with the negative vibes. That was always your downfall when we were kids. You're always so negative. Be positive! Send out the positive vibes!"

I shrugged my shoulders. I suppose I had nothing else better to do. And I had to admit, I had nothing much to lose thanks to my divorces because my third ex had taken me to the cleaner's big time. And, who knows, I could make a few bob. But why did I have a bad feeling about this caper I wonder?

"Just a minute, who's looking after money?" I ask.

My mate's face goes suddenly all angelic, "Why, me of course."

"Why you?"

My mate suddenly looks all hurt and upset. "Why? Don't you trust me?"

Now there was a very short answer to this, and I said it. "No!!!"

"So that's what you think of your best mate?" he says with this hurt puppy dog face. "You're showing your true colours. After all I've done for you. This is a stab in the back."

Now I had to think hard about that one, very hard in fact. "Just a minute," I jumped in quick, "like what have you done for me?"

My mate was wracking his brain now. "Well, well, what about that bike I gave you when we were kids?"

"That was over 50 years ago. I think we were about eight years old. And that bike was a death trap," I snapped back, "I was doing about sixty miles an hour bombing down the flyover, when the brakes failed and the front wheel fell off. I spent two days in hospital with concussion and my leg and arm in plaster thanks to you."

"You see, you're at it again, being negative. I give you a bike, and you blame me for breaking your wrist. You're so ungrateful Terry."

"Just a minute! You didn't give me it. You sold me it for thirty bob. And you'd nicked it."

"Details, details, mere details," insists my mate. "I'm trying to make us some money here, and you're throwing my help back in my face." His expression goes all limp, and I'm sure I detect tears in his eyes. He could win an Oscar when it comes to acting.

"I have to say Terry. You've really hurt me, thinking I would rob you."

"Alright, alright you'll be getting the violins out next." But I did warn him and clenched my fist and put it to his nose, "You pull a fast one Achmed, and I'll do you."

"So it's agreed?" says my mate, quickly back to his fast talking ways. "I look after the money?"

I grudgingly agree. "I suppose so, but I'll be watching the airports. So no holidays to Switzerland."

A broad smile crossed my mate's face again, now that we were good bosom buddies again.

"So you start writing and I'll give my mate the publisher a bell." He downs his second can of lager in one gulp, burps and disappears out my front door like a fart in a storm. I sigh and shake my head. What was I getting myself into?

Now I've never been a man of letters, and I had my doubts I could string two words together that might be of any interest to any one else, let alone write a book anyone might be interested in reading, let alone paying good money for it.

So after great misgivings about the whole thing, I reluctantly started putting pen to paper and before I know it, I'm burning the midnight oil and I am surprising myself. And the word count starts adding up, and memories are flooding back to me, and I suddenly realize my dodgy mate is right, I do have one hell of a story to tell about my days as a Rod Stewart lookalike.

Over the next few months I'm driving our lass round the bend, because I'm sat there writing and in stitches of laughter as I write. I found I was getting obsessed and even in bed in the middle of the night, I would be thinking of something funny that happened to me, and I would start laughing in bed and waking our lass up and she would blurt out angrily, "I'm sure you're going nuts."

And sometimes I was in such stitches of laughter in bed, that the bed would start to shake, with the headboard banging on the wall, and the neighbor would bang on the wall shouting: "Give it a bleedin' rest will ya, I've got to get up for work."

I solved that one by pulling the bed away from the wall, but I was still pissing off our lass with my midnight hysterics, and she would get up with a growl.

"I'm pissed off with this, I'm sleeping in the other room. You're nuts and so is that bloody mate of yours. Bloody Rod Stewart. I bet his wife doesn't have to put up with this!"

So for the next few months I would sleep alone, having these periodic bouts of midnights hysterics, as all these funny incidents flooded back to me, and I would find myself charging out of bed to write something down so I wouldn't forget it by the morning.

My dodgy mate had given me this pen and note pad with the instructions: "Take it where ever ya' go, because you will remember something funny, and if you don't write it down, you'll forget it." That was good advice.

So one day, me and the wife are out shopping, having a cup of coffee in some café in town, and suddenly I would think of some funny incident, and I just can't help myself and I burst out into hysterics. And our lass would slowly sink down in her chair, as people started to look at me like I was the Mad Hatter as I sat there feverishly scribbling away.

It went on like this for months and I think our lass was close to booting me out the front door if I didn't change my ways. But I was hooked by now on this writing game, day and night I was working on it. My dodgy mate would come round on one of his flying visits, scoop up my latest piece and disappear like a genie in a puff of smoke. "The publisher just loves it," he would say, going out the front door as quickly as he came in. "He's laughing his head off. Keep up the good work." He would leave with the words, "I'll be back," hanging ominously in the air.

By six months of this routine I'm done, the script has been edited and read and re-read to death, and even a lawyer had looked it over. I'm waiting on tenterhooks for my mate to turn up to bring the first printed book. As good as his word, my mate charges in all excited and pushes the finished glossy product proudly under my nose.

And I can't believe it. I am holding a book that I have written, and the front cover glares back at me with the words, **"I WAS ROD STEWART'S DOUBLE."** With a subtitle of, **"The Sordid confessions of a Rod Stewart Lookalike."**

"Just a minute," I pipe up, "What's this, 'The Sordid confessions of a Rod Stewart Lookalike? What's sordid about it?"

"Are you kidding me?" my mate booms back, "it's nothing but shagging from start to finish, ya dirty little Tyke. I've got to hand it to ya' Terry mate. You were one hell of a perv mate."

I shrug my shoulders and concede the point. I look again at this glossy book in my hand. And there is my name in lights across the book cover- BY TERRY COX. "Bloody hell, I'm a published author now."

"Good innit?" my mate smiles back.

"Do you think Rod Stewart will find out?" I ask nervously.

"I bloody hope so," says my mate, "I posted one off a week to my mate who lives in Los Angeles, and he's gonna post it through his door."

"Well don't be winding Rod Stewart up!" I say, swallowing with a hard, nervous gulp.

"Ah you worry too much, Rod Stewart will love it, I bet."

Well the dastardly deed is done and now it's over to you readers for your verdict and don't forget to put a good review on Amazon for me.

And any day now I'm expecting a letter from Rod Stewart's solicitor. Just a minute, where has my dodgy mate gone?!!

So cheers Rod, I certainly couldn't have it written without you. (2017) Photo by courtesy of Hull Daily Mail publications. And since I don't have the money to keep up with your good looks Rod, I am now doing lookalike appearances as Worzel Gummidge.

CHAPTER ONE

"And it's the mid 1970s. And the aftermath of a Rod Stewart Lookalike party."

Oh my God what a bloody night, is this hangover for real or am I dead? My head feels like a back yard metal bucket that somebody is banging on with a lump hammer. My mouth feels like a camel's scrotum after trudging for five days in the hot desert sun, and I can feel myself wanting to fart, but daren't in case I follow through. So I squeeze my buttocks together and force the fart back whilst I take stock of where I am, who I am and just how the fuck I got here.

I slowly open my eyes and the room is still spinning and spinning, and I can feel my guts bubbling and I'm ready to throw up. Boy, did I tie one on last night. I must've had a great time, if only I could remember any of it. I know I'm in a bed somewhere but have no idea where, and can't recall how the hell I got here.

"Gently, gently does it now, Terry me old mate," I whisper to myself, whilst I try and get my bearings. Slowly, I struggle to open my eyes and I am staring back at myself in a dressing table mirror. Death warmed up is staring back at me. I look like shit on a bad day. With a big intake of breath to hold back the puke trying to get out, I try and lift my head off the pillow to look around, and again everything is spinning and I let out a loud aching groan.

My legs hurt, my arms hurt, in fact it seems every bone in my body is aching and throbbing. Another look in mirror and I can see I have a black eye. "What the hell happened?" I asked myself aloud and feel the bruise under my eye and it's painful.

I just about have enough brain cells left that are working to realize I am in a hotel room, but where? That is the big question. So I throw back the covers and go for it and swing my legs out the bed and hold my head in my hands as the room has started spinning again, and again I feel the need to throw up. I swear a silent oath that I will never do this again. It seems it's a promise I just can't keep to myself once the party's started, and as usual the booze is free, and the birds swarming around me in abundance and gagging for it. I just can't help myself. I'm like a kid that has been locked in sweet shop and I just gorge on all the 'goodies' I can. I just throw caution to the wind with gay abandon once I've got the first few glasses of booze down my neck, and there's just no stopping me. Then, as usual, I just go over the top, and I am ending up like this far too often. I keep promising myself I have to slow down but I soon forget the promises to myself once the free 'hemlock'starts flowing and the hot young and tight fair maids are pressing their nubile bodies on me. After all, life takes no prisoners, and as my ship mate often says, "No one get's out of this life alive." A pretty good motto really and I was young then, and like most young kids, my brain was in my pants as they say, and I was banging birds ten to the dozen with the pick of the bunch, and who did I have to thank for it, but Rod Stewart. I'll explain as you read.

I might not have Rod Stewart's money but I'm certainly getting a lot of perks in the bird department and that's thanks to Rod, with a little help from mammy and daddy of course.

Speaking of birds, as I sit on the edge of the bed in the middle of this disaster of a hotel room Rod Stewart would have been proud of, I realize I'm in my birthday suit and next to me on the bed is a body beneath the covers with the top of a blond head just sticking out. The whiff of this strong perfume suddenly assaults my senses and the need throw up becomes overwhelming. I just hope what lies beneath snoozing and dead to the world does not have a six o'clock shadow. Whoever is under the covers I certainly couldn't remember if I had given her one, let alone who she was. I give it a little thought as to who it might be, shake my head as I have no idea and walk gingerly and still starkers with the room swaying into the bathroom, stepping over another anonymous duvet-covered body laid out cold in the land of nod on the floor. Gagging, I sick my guts up and then in some haste I plonk my arse onto the bog and 'drop the kids off' with a long spluttering bluster that echoes around the hotel bathroom. What a relief that was as the bloated dastardly anal gases blast out of my arse as I pebble dash the toilet pan and I feel my bloated guts deflate with such a blast of satisfaction. I breathe a massive sigh of heavenly relief. "Ahhhhh!"

For a few lost moments I just sit swaying precariously on the pot like an entranced nude garden gnome waiting for more gastric relief. By this time, I could hear the slow regretting moans and groans of stirrings coming from the bedroom, and they certainly sounded like I felt.

By now, it was all slowly coming back me as I stared at myself sitting on the pot in the bathroom mirror. It was not a pretty sight.

The hangover fog in my alcohol-frazzled brain was gradually beginning to clear, and flashes of the night before were zinging through my brain. It was only then that I realized someone was asleep in the bath covered with a blanket over his head muffling his snores. So, after wiping my third eye out, I pulled back the cover for a peek and it was my none other than my 'workmate' and partner in crime Elvis Presley. Now when I say Elvis Presley, I don't mean the real Elvis Presley, I mean a lookalike. His real first name was Joe, and for a day job he was a bus driver from Essex in his other life. I assure you this will all start to make sense as we go along. Just hang on in there readers.

Seeing Elvis in the bath helped prompt more recollections of the previous night's foggy events. They were coming back in dribs and drabs, and come to think of it, I now vaguely remembered who was under the covers in the bed. Well, I knew it was a bird at least.

Elvis groggily popped his head up with all the speed of an Amazonian sloth, "Oh my fucking head," was all he managed to say with a big groan, "how much did we have to drink last night?"

"Tell me about it mate," I groaned back, "I am never doing that again," I promised aloud.

"Yeah right," he groaned back. "I've heard that one before."

"No, no," I insisted grimly, "I mean it this time. I can't go through this again."

By the way, to you readers out there, I think I should introduce myself. My name is Terry Cox, and for my sins and a few extra bob in the back hand tax-free, wink, wink, say no more, apart from being a merchant seaman for my day job, I do the odd number for this London lookalike agency, as, now wait for it, a Rod Stewart lookalike. Over the years it's been an interesting time. I've had an absolute surreal ball of time pretending to be Rod Stewart, and found myself being paid ridiculous amounts of dosh just to impersonate him when they can't afford the real thing. I don't sing or dance or anything, I just look like him they tell me. Although I have to admit in my worse drunken moments I have got up on stage, and made a fool of myself miming to Rod Stewart records karaoke-style. However, I mainly just appear at weddings, clubs and supermarket openings with other famous lookalikes, and basically get drunk on the free booze, and within limits, shag any bird offering herself up. Now please don't judge, remember this is the 1970's and I am in my twenties and young and stupid. Yes, there are many upsides to being a Rod Stewart lookalike. Although believe me, looking like Rod also has a few downsides too. And it's also got me into fights in pubs, clubs and other dodgy situations but generally the benefits far outweighed the disadvantages. I don't think the real Rod Stewart would mind that much, and I did once bump into him in the lounge at Heathrow Airport. I was flying out to catch a ship and he was flying to Los Angeles, as I remember. Anyway we had a really funny exchange of words I will tell you about in a later chapter. Rod Stewart is a genuinely very nice guy and was so amused by my hair and get up and being a lookalike. Yes, even when not doing a Rod Stewart lookalike gig, I always kept my hair styled like his and dressed like he did. I suppose I loved the attention, and birds just couldn't resist stopping me and on many occasions, as a merchant seaman, I found myself in many, many, many different countries. In fact, on my travels I've lost count of the countries I have travelled to and from, and from one end of the globe to other. I've been round the world a few times, and milked looking like Rod Stewart for all it was worth, especially with the birds and free stuff like free drinks and free hotel rooms galore in exchange for just sitting in the hotel lounge and talking to the guests. That happened a lot in foreign ports. My shipmates loved it as I would usually have a gaggle of frenzied girls chasing me down the streets, or being accosted in foreign pubs and bars. Of course, being young and full hormones, and the need to spread my seed far and wide as it were, I would usually end chatting one or two birds up and having my pick for a night of filth and animal debauchery. My ship mates would usually end up bedding down the leftovers and so they wouldn't complain. When I look back I wondered how I kept up the pace.

Of course Rod Stewart was, and still is, a massive internationally-known star and famous face. I found I couldn't go anywhere without stares or being stopped by the curious. Older people would want photographs with me, or to buy me drinks or just autographs. I mean, I suppose I could have put a stop to it straight away by not trying to look and dress like him, but why would I? The fact was, I loved the attention, especially from the girls. I mean, just think about this for a moment. I had none of the problems usually associated with chatting up girls. You know the type of stuff, whether a girl fancied you or not, and the risk of getting the bum's rush if you tried chatting one up. They would chat me up, in fact many a time, I just could not get rid of them. They were great days, and I was at a young enough age to take full advantage. It began to get like a game to me. I admit it, I enjoyed the attention. I mean what's not to enjoy? I was young and sowing my wild oats, and I suppose a little selfish and thoughtless as you are when you are in your twenties. I look back now, and being older and wiser, I think of some of the absolutely beautiful girls who threw themselves at me because I looked like Rod Stewart, and I would just simply cast many aside, after banging them of course. I know I sound a bit of a big head to many reading this, but I was very young then and this Rod Stewart thing had made me a bit arrogant, and let's be truthful, I wasn't doing anything that any other young guy in their twenties wouldn't be doing given half the chance.

It's strange though, when you're having fun and good times, it does seem to make time go much faster, and those days of my misspent youth did seem to go in a blink of eye. At that moment in time, I seemed to have everything I wanted. I had the job I always wanted as a merchant seaman, and was getting paid to travel the world. And for me every port I sailed to seemed to bring another adventure, and of course the Rod Stewart 'thing' I played for all it was worth.

Foreign birds especially would always get carried away. Many of them just wanted you to be Rod Stewart, even if they knew really you weren't, they would just fool themselves. It was like a charade, a game. I suppose it would be something for the girls to brag about to their friends, that they had shagged Rod Stewart. As for me, most of the time I just went along with charade and cashed in with the sex with some really beautiful girls.

Blonde Swedes especially in my opinion are the most beautiful birds in the world. And in the 1970s the birds in Sweden were Rod Stewart nuts. But you name the country and I've filled my boots there.

Sometimes it got a bit hairy when you have ten or twenty girls chasing you down a street. I mean in those days, like any young guy, I liked the ladies, but there is something really scary when a gang of screaming women are running after you.

One time in Stockholm in Sweden we had just berthed and the ship was laying over for a few days while we unloaded and then took on cargo. I was just minding my own business and had gone shopping with a couple of the ship's crew into the centre of Stockholm. It used to start first with stares, girls whispering and then pointing, and then some gorgeous blonde Swedish bird would stop me and ask me for an autograph with a big white toothy smile that would just melt you. Those Swedish birds are something else. It's the silky blonde hair, but it's not so much blonde as bordering on this near white golden colour, mostly long straight and shiny. They also had such smooth almost faultless skin like alabaster. Yes, give me Swedish girls any day.

Now I didn't speak Swedish but most Swedes speak a cute type of English. So on this day a stunning young Swedish schoolgirl approaches me, and in this giggly broken English voice asks if I'm Rod Stewart and I say, "No." Now this girl is way too young for me, but anyway she doesn't believe me, and takes out one her school books and asks me to sign it. Now I would get asked all the time to sign autographs or pose with them for pictures. It usually got to the stage where it was pointless arguing because they had got it into their heads I was Rod Stewart, mainly because they wanted me to be Rod Stewart, and so I would end up signing an autograph for them, if anything just to get rid of them.

In the 1970s Sweden was one of most unbelievably beautiful countries in the world, and the people so uniquely friendly. This one scary incident started after this one young Swedish school girl I just described had stopped me in the street and asked me for my autograph, and would not take no for an answer. I was with a couple of the young lads from the ship, and they always thought it amusing, and were eyeing her up from the back and generally perving on her, as young merchant seaman do. These two crew were sixteen-year-old galley boys and not much older than this Swedish girl. I must admit she did look a lot older than the school uniform she was wearing. Anyway, I did my good deed for the day and after signing this lovely girl's school book she wants a kiss. In fact she is insisting on a kiss. Now as I said, this young girl was far too young for me so I smiled very politely and declined. Now Swedish birds are not backward in coming forward, and are renowned for being the most sexually liberated in Europe. Before I knew it, she had thrown her arms around my neck and was sploshing her lips all over me with a big wet kiss. Her arms were tightly wrapped around my neck and she was hanging onto to my face like a sink plunger. My ship mates were in hysterics and people walking by thought it also highly amusing but I didn't. I mean in the UK, having a young school girl in her school uniform hanging around the neck of a 24-year-old man smothering him with a passionate kiss, in the middle of a crowded street at best would have got me arrested, or at least frowned on by passers-by. However, they certainly think differently in Sweden about this type of thing. Instead of attracting disapproving looks, most people nearby seemed to find it funny.

It wasn't a laughing matter for me and I pulled this girl off and gave her a 'big brother' talking to, telling her to get on her way. My mates were still rolling about. This girl just looked up at me with a big cheeky smile and despite being sent on her way with a sharp word or two she just smiled again and waltzed away with a girly skip in her step. I glared at my mates who were still laughing. "It's not funny, that's jail bait."

"It's Sweden mate," the first galley boy answered with a snigger, "sex is the national sport here."

"I prefer them a little older," I told him with a degree of outrage in my voice.

Well if I thought it was the end of the matter, oh my God was I was wrong or what? Suddenly my mate is looking across the road and pointing. He has a slight look of amused horror on his face, and I turn my gaze in the direction of what my ship mate is pointing at. Now to my own horror, I take a big gulp at the sight of the little Swedish school girl coming back in my direction. What's worse, she's not alone. She has a charging, screaming horde of other school girls with her and they are closing in on me fast. I don't know what they are shouting and screaming as it's all in Swedish but they seem to be picking up numbers as they head in my direction. "Fucking hell!"

In situations like this, famous people are surrounded by bodyguards. But me, all I had were two crew members with me, and looking at the size of this frenzied Swedish mob heading fast towards me, I imagined they would not hold them off for long, leaving me trampled underfoot, after being ragged and rived to death. My heart started pounding with real fear and in total panic all three of us started to run. Would you believe it, my two crew mates took off in the opposite direction to me. I was being chased through Stockholm on my own, with a mad, out of control tribe of what looked like savage Viking school girls chasing me, hoping to do God knows what, if and when they caught up with me. I didn't look back and ran for my life but from what I could hear behind me, they closing fast and all I could hear were chants of "ROD STEWART! ROD STEWART!"

My heart was now pounding so hard it was almost coming through my chest. For one of the few times in my life I was genuinely scared, wondering whether this Rod Stewart thing needed a lot more thought. However, this was neither the time or the place for deep thought. Instead all I could think about was that if they caught up with me, I would be lucky to get out of alive, or at least without great injury.

By now my chest was almost bursting and I ran into this small shop out of breath and panting like a race horse. I slammed the door shut with a great crash and leaned on the door with all my might. The man behind counter must have thought I was going to rob him and he ran in panic into the back and locked himself behind a door which he slammed shut. Suddenly the crowd of girls were shooting passed the front door and their numbers seemed endless. It wasn't just school girls shooting past the door but other women just screaming as they were running. It was a wild mob. If they caught up with me, I knew I would be a gonner. I was in panic looking for some locks or bolts on the door. Then all of a sudden I look through this door, and two girls with a mad frenzied stares on their faces are staring back at me through the glass. They've spotted me. One of them points at me and screams like a banshee and they charge the door. I am leaning on it with all my might, but suddenly more girls have joined pushing on the door, and then more and they are all screaming, "ROD STEWART!! ROD STEWART!!!"

Then suddenly all I can see is this out-of-control horde of crazy girls and women in the street outside. There is a sea of them looking slightly mad and very determined. Then they are charging the shop door. I am pushing with all my might but I can't hold them back, and the door is slowly being pushed open. Suddenly I can't hold it anymore and I am thrown back as the door crashes open. Landing on the floor, this mad horde of females are on me and frenzied hands are all over me. I'm not sure if I'm being punched, touched up, groped or what but their hands are everywhere pulling at me and several of them are astride my chest. Now to some people, drowning in a sea of crazed Swedish girls might seem bliss but at that particular moment in time I was not one of them. I can feel my shirt being torn off and a frenzy of hands are pulling and pushing me, and now, "Oh my God," I can feel my jeans being pulled off while others are pushing their lips on me. I'm being held down on all sides, with girls grabbing and groping me all over and they are climbing over me, and one of them stands on my nuts and I scream out. I can now feel my jeans being pulled down and I am trying to tug them back up, but it's like being in the middle of an out-of-control rugby scrum. Just as I feel I cannot hold on much longer and the lights are about to go out I hear the whine of police sirens and cars screeching outside. There is a lot of screaming, shouting and bawling and suddenly, I have never in all my life been so happy to see a copper's face. There was still a riot going on in this shop but one by one the police push this crowd of girls out the door. By the time the cops had cleared the place I was laid out on the floor with my shirt torn off my back, my shoes and sock were gone and the top of my jeans were ripped and half way around my knees. I am covered in bruises and my face is scratched. I look up in a daze and this group of Swedish coppers are staring down at me, one of them with a big smile on his face. "Ahhhh, yes," he says "Rod Stewart!" The coppers all start laughing. While I was glad to see them, I was not so amused as the cops helped up and sat me on a chair. There was still this almighty crowd of screaming and screeching women outside, and other cops were outside holding them off. The owner had now surfaced from his sanctuary in the back room and very kindly gave me a glass of water and a gentle pat of concern on the shoulder. Considering half of his small shop had been trashed I think he took it all quite well really. But Swedes are like that, they have this tremendous sense of unselfishness and go out of their way to show kindness and always put others first. Yes, the Swedes are the best.

Now all that was left to do was for the cops to get me out of this shop to a of place safely. With my shoes and socks gone and no shirt to speak of, one them gave me his leather police flying jacket to put on and the shop owner handed me a pair of slippers that were two sizes too big. The shop blinds were pulled down to avoid the prying eyes of the now massive crowd outside and I was spirited out the back, but not before I had signed autographs on cops' note books and had a photograph taken with my arm around the shop owner. Yes, after all the trouble I had inadvertently caused, the Rod Stewart effect was still going on.

Now I don't know how that photograph turned out but I expected I looked quite a sight, all battered and torn, wearing a Swedish cop's leather bomber jacket and massive pair of slippers with a face full of scratches, cut and bruises and covered in lipstick. In fact, later I discovered I had lipstick in some very odd places, if you know what I mean.

After insisting I go to the hospital to be checked over, the cops gave me a full VIP escort with two motorcycle outriders and sirens screaming. They took me straight back to the ship, and with sirens still screaming they pulled up at the gang plank. By now the whole crew had turned out turn out on deck to see what all the commotion was about. Bedraggled like one of the war-wounded, I limped up the gang plank with the crew laughing and generally taking the piss. My two errant buddies who had done a runner earlier were waiting to greet me at the top. I was not best pleased with them, to say the least. "What the fuck happened to you two?" I snapped at them angrily. One of them looked at me trying to hide a grin. "Are you kidding me? There were hundreds of them."

The other said: "We just ran. We didn't know you would run in the opposite direction."

"Looks like they caught up with you then," he added with a smirk, and both of them started sniggering.

I limped onto the deck. "What do you think? Thanks for all your help. I could've been killed, no thanks to you."

"Oh come on Tez, it wasn't our fault, mate. Rod Stewart's got a lot to answer for." Both the bastards burst out laughing. "You didn't get your leg over then 'Rod'!" It was now full-on piss-taking mode.

"Very funny," I growled back. With that, the whole crew were taking the piss. I knew I would never hear the end of it. I sneered at them with the contempt they deserved and

I limped to my cabin, leaving the crew highly amused. I would get the piss-taking in the neck all week.

In those days, if Sweden was famous for one thing around the world it was having the most unbelievably stunning, knock-out beautiful blond girls. Of course, the other famous thing Sweden was known for in those days was its porn movies, or as we called them 'blue films'. Being in the merchant navy, ships were always full of porn magazines and blue films and mostly they were Swedish. Whenever we docked in Sweden we would have blokes coming on board trying to flog porn. Selling porn to merchant seamen was big business in places like Sweden, and nobody made porn movies, as full-on dirty as the Swedes. So for many merchant seaman, Sweden always held a special place in their hearts as a place where you could get your leg over in great abundance. On the docksides we would always get a parade of very beautiful Swedish prostitutes swaggering up and down showing off their wares to watching sailors. I was always a bit old-fashioned when it came to prostitutes and never availed myself of their services but many did. I had heard far too many horror stories of the consequences of using such services so always gave them a wide berth. But on principle I would never pay for sex anyway, since in my Rod Stewart alter ego I got more than my fair for free anyway.

As I have stated earlier, you readers have to continually bear in mind when reading about my escapades, that I was only twenty-odd years old. Being young and stupid, what had just happened to me being savaged by a horde of crazy school girls, had been a lucky escape. It was a rude awakening to the dangers I had never seen before. I was just enjoying being Rod whenever I could. I mean, I had previously had bad experiences in my lookalike role but never encountered anything like that. Not on that scary scale anyway. I still liked the attention, but I would have to think hard about this. If the cops hadn't rescued me, I dread to think what might have happened.

And I was left with thought, "Aren't people weird?" Or maybe I was just being naïve, and not realizing in certain circumstances I was playing with fire. I would definitely have to be more careful in future. After my bad experience I did tone down the Rod Stewart thing a bit, hiding my hair with a baseball cap. I even took to wearing sun glasses and sometimes let the stubble grow a bit. But of course, being young, you soon forget and complacency soon started to creep in again. Slowly but surely I was soon back in full Rod Stewart lookalike mode because, more than anything, I was missing the attention.

CHAPTER TWO

When I was doing my Rod Stewart lookalike number, obviously if I was appearing at some posh do they would expect me to have my hair like his, and so yes, I used to get my hair done at only top-notch salons. The woman who owned the agency I worked for was a real stickler for detail like that. She had many other famous lookalikes on her books - Queen Elizabeth II, Elvis Presley, Clint Eastwood as Dirty Harry. You name a lookalike and I met them at one time or another at some party or other. The agency owner was a real task master when it came to detail and she would inspect us all before we attended any party or event to make sure we were all up to scratch in the lookalike department.

When it came to me being Rod Stewart, she always insisted I wore those really tight, crutch-gripping, ball bag-squashing, leopard-skin drainpipe jeans that Rod used to wear in his heyday years. Now these jeans were real ball crushers and in the 'three-piece sweet department' I've always been a big lad if you get my drift. The ball bag area of these tight jeans stuck out like I had a coppers truncheon down the front of my trousers. But according to the boss, the ladies liked that sort of thing, and orders are orders, as they say.

She was right about the ladies liking a bulging pouch, and many a time I had been seated at some posh party next to some randy bird, and just as I'm tucking into the free nosh, a hand would wonder under the table and start squeezing my equipment with gay abandon. I would look at this bird next to me with a big smile on her face, as she secretly pulled my plonker under the table. By this time, things would be stiffening up, as by now she is pulling on me like a milk maid milking a Jersey cow. So I'm sat there in throes of pleasure trying to look normal, as she is riving away on my pork truncheon under the table.

Now when it came to stuff like this, the boss took a very dim view, if you got caught. How the hell you were supposed to object to very assertive female sexual advances when you are surrounded by hundreds of guests, I don't know. But the boss was always a stickler and insisted on a 'No bonking the clients' policy and if she found out, you were on your bike with no questions asked. It didn't just happen to me, it was just one of the hazards of the job, if you can call it that.

Now this next story should tickle you, I know it did me. I was laughing for weeks and never got fed up of telling this one.

One time at this big posh shindig, the whereabouts of which will remain nameless, my mate Joe the Elvis lookalike is getting the eye of this gorgeous blond bird sat opposite him next to this bloke with a beard.

So anyway, my Elvis lookalike mate is just sat there minding his own business and tucking into the free nosh, when suddenly someone under the table is fiddling with his flies, and then has their hands in his pants and he finds himself getting a blow job underneath the table as he was about to tuck into his starter. My mate told me that he noticed that the blond bird that who had been opposite him, was suddenly gone. Naturally, he has these visions of this blond bird under the table sucking on him like a vacuum pump. By now whoever is under the table is going up gears and she is giving him the full business as he is sat there, with eyes glaring open, head nodding in ecstasy and trying to look all innocent. Finally, after being sucked like a choc ice, it's job done and my Elvis mate deflates as the pleasure subsides.

My mate is telling me all this the next morning at breakfast but there is an odd look on his face.

"I don't know what you are complaining about," I tell him, "that blond bird was gorgeous."

"Well that's the problem," my mate slowly answers back, "While I am in the full throes sexual pleasure, thinking the blond bird is under the table, suddenly as I am about to shoot my bolt and she walks up and sits down opposite me."

I was totally intrigued by now. "So who was under the table then?"

Did my mate get the shock of his or what? Some minutes later when he looked across the table, and this bloke with a beard was sat there smiling at him in what was the other empty chair. "And he winked at me," said my mate in shock. I never stopped laughing for a week when he told me. Needless to say Joe (Elvis) didn't find it so funny at all and he swore me to secrecy. "Cross my heart and hope to die," I promised, but I just couldn't keep my mouth shut. It was just so funny.

I worked with a lot of female lookalikes too. One who was the absolute double of Debbie Harry, and she was bloody gorgeous, and sexier even than the real McCoy. Her body was just so amazing and so sleek, and just like the real Debbie Harry, she fitted into her sexy black silk dress like a tight surgical glove. Debbie's problem wasn't her looks, it was her mouth and she gave the game away as soon as she opened it. She was a real blond bimbo in the brains department but she could talk the hind legs off a donkey if you got her onto her one specialist subject: 'Life behind the counter of a long distance lorry drivers' greasy spoon café'. Yes, real gripping stuff I can tell you, and what made it worse listening to her was that she had a voice like a high-pitched squeaky fog horn and just as loud. Once she had a few drinks down her neck and got going, nothing - and I mean nothing - would shut her up until she had bored you to death and you were ready to slash your wrists. Once she had got a few more jars down her neck, she would throw caution to the wind and would start chucking herself around the dance floor, throwing her arms legs about like some wild Zulu dancer. In drunken states like this she often embarrassed us all, and often ended up on the stage doing a karaoke session as Debbie Harry and bellowing out a Blondie number like a Canadian mountain moose with hernia, "Once had love and it was a gas, soon found it was heart of glass..." she would belt out tunelessly and slowly this skin-tight, little black silk mini skirt number would start to rise up her legs, until the full throttle gusset of her skimpy knickers was showing off a thigh gap as wide as the Blackwall Tunnel. While her version of Heart of Glass left a lot to be desired, God did she have one hell of a body. The watching men in the audience would be salivating in a frenzy of drunken clapping and wolf whistling as they egged her on and her skimpy dress rose further and further up her legs as she pranced about on the stage.

As I said my mate Joe was a real dead ringer for Elvis in the face department. He had though, one big drawback being an Elvis lookalike, he was only five foot, five inches tall, and the real Elvis was six feet tall. Joe had to make up for the lack of height by wearing these six-inch heel platform boot clod-hoppers that Gary Glitter would have been proud of. By the way, that's the last time I will mention Gary Glitter, although I did once work with a Glitter lookalike - nuff said.

Now my mate Joe, the lookalike Elvis had a few other 'small' but significant deficiencies as well in the Elvis lookalike department. I didn't like to point them out, as Joe was conscious of them anyway, but since I haven't seen him for over 35 years I'm sure he won't mind if I let them out now. Elvis Joe was also as bald as a coot, apart from one of those 'beards' on the back of his head if you get my meaning. I think it's called male-pattern baldness. So Joe had to wear this big black bouffant wig that put another three inches on his height. It looked more like one those bearskins that Queens Household Guards wore on parade. If Joe came back to the hotel drunk after a gig he would usually crash out on the bed fully clothed and by the time he woke up the next morning, complete with his full five o'clock shadow and Elvis wig, he would look more like a demented Wolf Man than an Elvis lookalike.

To add to Joe's lookalike troubles, he also had a bit of a beer belly paunch that he would try to hide by keeping it tucked in with this girdle underneath his white Elvis white rhinestone one-piece suite with all these cheap and tacky gold-painted medallions hanging around his neck that he bought from some car boot sale. The bell bottoms of this white one-piece suit would be wide enough at the bottom to camouflage his massive clod-hopping platform heels. The white one-piece suit though was really far too tight a squeeze for a mere mortal, to tell you the truth. It all looked a bit too painful to me and he would half zip-up the front of this Rhinestone Elvis suite so he could show off his false spray-on hairy chest.

Me and Elvis often shared a hotel room if we were doing a party gig together, and we would both sit in front of the dressing table mirrors like a couple of tarts putting on our make-up ready to play our parts. Elvis really should have got a bigger costume, because it was just far too tight a fit, and he always looked like he was about to explode from the internal pressure by the time he had wrestled and squeezed into it. It was pure agony for Joe getting into this white one-piece monkey suite. But if Joe was anything, he was a consummate professional and took his lookalike job so seriously and went to extremes to get the look right. I was much more light hearted and just didn't take it too seriously. I could earn a lot of extra cash, then there were the birds and shag galore. It was a bit of youthful fun to me. I just saw the whole lookalike thing as a bit of pantomime.

But as Joe would often say to me, "It's alright for you. You don't have try and look like Rod Stewart, you do look like him. It's hard work for me."

He wasn't kidding about his preparation for his Elvis role and I would get roped into the preparation. Many a time I often found myself standing on Elvis's bed, with one foot pushing on his arse while Elvis laid on the bed, and I would be pulling like crazy on the strings of this girdle attempting to get Elvis's beer belly as flat as a pan cake so he could fit into his white suite. And when we were eventually done, and I was sweating like Turkish wrestler with the effort, Elvis would stand proudly looking at himself in the mirror, brush himself down with a painful self-satisfied smile, and walk away sort of slowly, one careful step at a time, more gingerly clodding along than

walking really, with all the uncultured grace of a
Frankenstein monster that had shit itself. His corset was
usually too tight, and the height on the platforms boots
hardly helped his balance either I think. And I don't why,
but the tightness of the corset, seemed to push out his
arse, and it all looked a bit unbalanced to me.

Just before going out the hotel door Joe would gingerly
turn around, look at me and say, "Well, what do ya think
Tez?" as if asking for my approval.

And I would tip my head and wink, "You look great Joe,"
and I would let out a little phony laugh, "I mean Elvis."
What a fucking liar I was but Joe would give me a thumbs
up. "You look great too Tez," he would say with an equally
phony smile and add with another phony smile, "I mean
Rod. I'll see ya down there then,"

And out the door Elvis would go to join the party
downstairs, mumbling: "My fucking back's killing me.
Why can't Elvis be five foot four, the lanky bastard." Then
he was gone he was gone out of the hotel bedroom.

Just as the door closes I hear this thud and Joe is shouting
for help. I dash out and Elvis is on the floor flat on his back
and he can't bend to get up, "Er mate gives a hand will ya
Tez?" says Elvis laid out as flat and stiff as a six by two
plank of wood.

So I get my hands under his armpits and heave, but I can't
lift him. Luckily, help is at hand in the shape of the Alvin
Stardust lookalike, all togged up in his tight black leathers
and just coming out of his room. "What the bleedin' 'ell is
going on?" says Alvin. "Fucking hell he's not pissed already
is he?"

"It's Joe, he's fallen over and he can't get up," I say as I'm
still heaving, "Give us a hand will ya mate."

"What in this??" says Alvin gesturing to his own tight black leather one-piece suit. "I can hardly bend myself." Despite his protests, Alvin Stardust lends a hand, and we both heave and Elvis rises in one solid piece like a sheet of stiff hardboard and we have him back on his feet, and he is swaying on these platform heels. I can't help thinking you could push him over with one finger. "You aright mate?" I asked Elvis, now back on his feet. It's thumbs up from Elvis and he clods off to the lift with a steadying hand from Alvin Stardust. Just as I think it's safe to go back and finish dressing, bloody hell! Elvis falls over again with a big thud and cracks his head on the wall. This time no matter how me and Alvin Stardust heave, we can't get him up and then another lookalike mate comes out into the corridor to see what's going. It's Bert, the Clint Eastwood lookalike, and he's wearing a phony hand gun and shoulder holster under his arm just like Dirty Harry. Now Clint Eastwood is another dead ringer lookalike. His real name is Bert and he's plumber from the East End of London. "Oh God," groans Clint. "Has Joe been at the sauce already?"

Joe the Elvis lookalike, as you have probably gathered by now, is a bit renowned for liking a drink or two and has this habit at parties of just filling his boots the gunnels. At midnight he just sort of goes all blank and keels over like falling great oak tree and we usually end up carting him back to his room before the boss get winds of what is going on.

"No I beedin' aren't been on the sauce," Elvis shouts back in protest, "It's these bleedin' platform heels."

And so all three of us start to heave Elvis up and Elvis is moaning and groaning in agony. "Go careful will ya lads," he protests, "this girdle is digging right in." And by now it is nearly time to go, and suddenly joining us on the corridor, is The Pope (The Polish Pope lookalike) in all his religious garb, with long white gowns and Papal hat, with a fag in one hand and glass of whiskey in the other.

"Oh God, is Joe pissed again?" groans the Pope. "If the boss sees him they'll be hell to pay." Just as those words leave his lips and would you believe it, the boss comes out of her room and is followed by Queen Elizabeth II in her royal gowns and crown on her head. The boss is almost spitting blood at the sight of us all trying to get Elvis on his feet.

"And before you say anything," Elvis announces aloud, "No, I'm not drunk."

"Then you had better get up then hadn't you," says the boss giving him short shrift.

So now there is me, as Rod Stewart, Clint Eastwood, Alvin Stardust and the Pope, all struggling to get Elvis back on his feet, with Queen Elizabeth II looking on supervising. Would you believe it, at that moment this paunchy America elderly couple come out their room. Now these two just look the part, and are a typical Mertal and Homer American types. They both just stand staring at this sight before them. Their eyes are like saucers and their mouths are hanging open. Slowly, they start to make their way past us but without taking their eyes of us. It's the Pope standing there, with this fag bobbing about in the corner of his mouth and his glass of whiskey in hand, who is the first to say something. He just looks at these two gob smacked old Americans and says: "Bless you my children" and makes the sign of the cross with his hand. Then Clint Eastwood gives them one of his Dirty Harry stares and says to the old man: "Well, do you feel lucky punk?!!". It was all in a joke but these two old Americans just never said a word and started to rush away in panic towards the lift without taking their eyes of us as they pushed past us with Elvis half on his feet. Suddenly they bolted like they were fleeing for lives but the old lady still took a moment to curtsey as she passed the Queen Elizabeth lookalike. We all just burst out laughing much to the boss's displeasure and I toddled off back into the hotel room to finish off my make-up – no catty comments please. What's good enough for Rod Stewart is good enough for me. So up yours!!!

CHAPTER THREE

Other lookalikes I have worked with in my time included Marilyn Monroe, Cary Grant, Rock Hudson and Peter Falk among others. The list is endless really. Some of them were the spitting image of the person they were imitating, and others not so good. I once met this amazing Clark Gable lookalike. He totally looked like Gable, he was the same height and build. And to add to this, he had actually mastered Clark Gable's voice. I must admit sometimes this guy confused even me. He was always winding up the boss with Clark Gable's famous one-liner from the film Gone With The Wind, and if the boss gave him a dressing down for anything, he would answer, "Frankly my dear, I don't give a damn." No matter how many times he said it, it always sounded so funny and we would all roll about laughing, even the boss couldn't hold back. Of all us lookalikes, Clark Gable was the favourite of the blue rinse older generation. At weddings and parties all the old ladies would crowd round him like geriatric groupies, and even some of these old biddies couldn't resist propositioning him with a quick cheeky grope.

It was not just the young birds by any means, and some of the older ones were just as bad, if the likes of a lookalike like Cary Grant, Clark Gable or Humphrey Bogart were on the guest list. But far the most popular lookalike with the old ladies was Clark Gable but he soon disappeared off the lookalike scene. The rumour was he had left his wife and kids and bunked up with some rich old boiler and moved to the south of France to live happy ever after as kept man. We heard that a year later the old bird had popped her clogs and left him a bundle and two big chateaus. I mean I too had my chances, especially with one rich bird, as you will read later.

Although my job as a merchant seaman took me away all over the world a lot, on leave I kept my hand in on the lookalike scene, as it was good fun, good cash-in-the-hand money, and the birds and sex were on tap almost. The Lookalike scene was like a small bazaar little community and with some like my mate Joe, The Elvis lookalike, we always stayed in touch, as Joe did some Lookalike business on the side without the boss knowing. So all in all, despite my intermittent sea trips, we bumped into each other all over the place at various lookalike events. And as I said, Joe the Elvis Lookalike was a bit of a dodgy character and used to organize his own events behind the boss's back, and often he would ring me up for one off jobs he had organized himself for a bit more cash in hand. They were not as up market events as the London agency, and some of the guvvy job parties Elvis organized left a lot to be desired.

Often they were Ladies or Hen Nights in working men's clubs or back street rough house spit and sawdust pubs. It was the Ladies and Hen Nights that were the worst, and often you took your life in your hands. Some of the women and young girls, once they'd had a bit of booze down them would go totally wild and lose all control. They would always end up groping you, and try tearing off your clothes.

One night me and Alvin Stardust got chased into the ladies'
toilet by this raving drunk Hen Party intent on gang-
banging me and Alvin. We ended up in this pub back yard
ladies' toilet barricading the door with empty beer barrels
and crates, with a pack of screaming drunken women on
the other side charging on the door. We only escaped with
our lives after climbing over the backyard wall and bolting
back to our hotel for sanctuary.

On one occasion Joe organized this guvvy job at this rough
arse Mansfield working men's club with me as Rod
Stewart, him as Elvis and Bert as Clint Eastwood.
I had a bad feeling about this joint the moment I walked
into the place. It was a spit and saw dust back street
boozer in this mining village just outside of Mansfield. It
was full of rather ferocious-looking inbred grunts, and that
was just the women. The type you get on the Jeremy Kyle
show, if you know what I mean.
We were only supposed to be putting in an appearance to
mingle so people could have photographs taken with us.
But stuff soon started to get out of hand as the little fat
bald-headed landlord thought he would try and get a bit
more mileage for the fee he was paying us. So anyway he
puts on the Karaoke machine. And then he pulled back
these grotty dirty curtains to unveil a small dilapidated
stage and announced, that Joe, the Elvis lookalike, had
agreed to give a rendition of the Elvis number Return to
Sender. And Joe's face was a sudden picture of horror
since he knew nothing about it.
So anyway, a big cheer went up around this place, and I
could see this look of total dread developing across Joe's
face because Joe couldn't sing, or dance. I didn't think Joe
was going to talk his way out of this one quickly, because

by now an unruly drunken mob of out-of-control old female boilers were surrounding him and pushing him towards the stage. I turned to my mate Bert, the Clint Eastwood Lookalike and we both grimaced.

"This should be interesting," I said out the side of mouth. "I think we should get closer to the door," Bert whispered back.

"We can't just leave Joe," I said back. "Remember you're Dirty Harry." It was a joke that did not go down well with Bert. "Very funny," Bert answered, "I have a bad feeling this could get ugly. Especially when he starts singing"

"What do you mean 'get ugly'" I answered, "have you seen those women."

"Yeah," said Clint with a nervy breath, "They could play for Featherstone Rovers."

"And win," I butted in.

And suddenly Joe, as Elvis, is on the stage and the club lights go out and a spotlight is suddenly switched on. And Joe is out there on the stage holding this microphone, and then the record Return To Sender starts blasting out and all the punters are up and bopping around the dance floor like a tribe of Red Indians doing a war dance.

But there is only music and no words, and Joe can't sing. The crowd start booing and jeering, and then to my amazement, Joe is suddenly swaying his hips just like Elvis, and pushing out his pelvis towards the women, his lip is doing the Elvis twitch, and they are just loving it, and he is singing too, if you can call it singing. He actually sounds more like Orson Wells having his balls squeezed, than Elvis, but it's working. But what came next even I didn't expect. These women are running onto the stage, screaming and groping Joe as they plant big kisses all over him. And then suddenly some woman throws a pair of knickers at him, and then another pair is thrown, but this time it's a big old pair of what looks like a dirty old women's bloomers, and they land on Elvis's head.

"Just a minute," I said looking at Clint in horror. "Where are they getting those knickers from?"

Clint just pointed. These women were taking off their knickers to throw and they were showing the lot. Believe me, these women were rough as a miner's arsehole, and it was not a pretty sight. There were hairy bushes and fat arses flashing everywhere.

The place is going wild now, and I have to give it to Joe, he's got these women eating out of his hand.

Now I've seen a video of the real Elvis in a situation like this, and usually the real Elvis catches a pair of knickers, wipes the sweat off his forehead and throws them back. But the knickers being thrown at Joe leave a lot to be desired in the hygiene department, and one inside out pair flying through the air look like the arse gusset is covered in a brown smudge, if you get my drift.

Now suddenly some of the women have grabbed me and Clint, and are dragging us to the dance floor. By this time, I detected the men in the pub are beginning to get ugly looks on their faces. There was Joe on the stage having well-worn knickers thrown at him, and me and Bert were being almost raped on the dance floor.

Then it suddenly turned into a nightmare as the beer took hold and the male punters started to get riled as the girls and women started just throwing themselves at us, and grabbing us for kisses, groping us and generally doing very dirty stuff.

By now the male grunts are off their seats and suddenly punches start getting thrown around. A massive punch-up ensues. Joe is dragged off the stage and all these blokes start laying into the three of us, just using us like punch bags.

Now as a merchant seaman, I've been in some spectacular bar room brawls in foreign ports I can tell you. Usually you are with the ship's crew and you all look out for each other. So I can handle myself given the right odds. But there were only three of us, me as Rod Stewart, Bert as Clint Eastwood and Joe as Elvis. As things panned out, it seemed Joe and Bert couldn't blow the froth off a pint of beer. Punches and boots were coming at me thick and fast in all directions, and I was being knocked from one end of this club to the other. I managed to stick the nut on one bloke who never got up again, and I belted this big bloke with a right hook that just seemed to make him smile. For my troubles he booted me right in the balls, so hard I was lifted me off my feet and as I curled up in agony, I felt him grab my shirt, and he literally launched me across the room, over some tables. I skidded across this glossy dance floor on my arse and ended up crashing through the door of the men's toilets, cracking my head with a big ding on one of the toilet pans. I was seeing stars by this time but I was on my feet quick as this bloke came pelting into the toilet to finish me off. I just quickly opened the door, and he ran full speed into the edge of it with a massive thud, sinking like a sack of shit to the floor. He was out cold with stars spinning around his head. When I ran back in, it was total pandemonium and the last I saw of the other two, was Elvis Joe in his white rhinestone one-piece suit flying through the air and landing on these tables with a crash, with Dirty Harry Bert not far behind him. To say we were getting murdered would have been a very apt description of how events were panning out that night. The little fat landlord had took to the stage and was trying to call for order over the microphone. But alas to no avail, and the last I saw of him, was when someone threw a red snooker ball at him. Whizzing through the air like a guided missile, it hit the landlord right smack on the noggin with a big painful sounding crack and he fell off the stage and onto a table of glasses sending them crashing and flying into a thousand pieces. He did manage to get back on his feet for a moment, and this big burly caveman type just launched him with a massive upper cut and lifted him off the floor. He went down again with a big thud and stayed down this time as his lights went out.

Thankfully help was soon at hand and the cavalry arrives with sirens blazing and blue lights flashing through the windows outside. A riot squad of cops charge in with truncheons drawn, and after a bit more blood and snot flying in all directions, we were saved from greater injury or even death by the timely intervention of the local plods. They say, there is never a copper around when you need one but that night I dread to think what would have been left of the three of us if not for the timely intervention of our glorious men in blue. After helping scrape our remains off the floors and walls, we were carted off to Mansfield Accident and Emergency in three ambulances. The last words on the sorrowful events of the night belongs to the landlord who is standing in the debris of what remains of his club, holding a dirty bar towel on his bleeding head. As I am being transported on a stretcher out the building like a battlefield casualty, this landlord bloke looks at me, and he says, "Who's gonna pay for the fucking damage then?"

Now my mate Elvis is usually the one known for his quick wit and repartee on occasions such as these. After years on the lookalike circuit, he has learned the subtle art of shutting up the piss takers. And I hear my mate, Elvis on another stretcher just ahead of me, laid with his white Elvis costume covered in blood, shouts back: "And fuck you too fatso!!" Yes, Elvis's comment did seem to sum up the success of the night.

But the evening was not a total disaster. At least the nurses and doctors on shift that night were highly amused at having the privilege of treating Elvis Presley, Rod Stewart and Clint Eastwood and we all ended up chatting up three nurses and ended up bunking down in the nurse's home for the night for a long night of 'painful' passion, as only nurses know how. In fact, thinking back, it was the only lookalike job where we didn't get paid, but going back to ask for our money didn't seem like a particularly good idea, in light of our hasty ambulance-assisted exit off the stage the night before. It put me off guvvy jobs for a time and if I did them after that, Bert always made sure we got the dosh first. But it certainly wasn't the last occasion I got a battering for looking like Rod Stewart. Generally, it was always the attention you would get off the birds that always kicked off the machos.

Yes, it wasn't always flattering attention you got, but that was just one of the hazards of the job. The lookalike who seemed to attract the most trouble was Clint Eastwood. I mean he was a hell of lookalike and totally looked the part, and the ladies and young birds loved him. I suppose because it was the heyday of the Dirty Harry movies, with all the macho image that went with it, there was always someone who wanted to prove themselves and brag about sticking one on Clint Eastwood.

By far the best lookalike of the lot was Her Majesty Queen Elizabeth II. I'm sure most of you readers out there will have seen her and I had to admit she was a fantastic dead ringer. I did a few gigs with The Queen with one agency I was with. If I remember rightly, her name was Jeannette Charles. She was such a good Queen Elizabeth II lookalike, the best I have seen on the lookalike scene, and a real celebrity in her own right. She actually had done a mass of films like The Naked Gun with Hollywood actors Leslie Nielson, Pricilla Presley and had done others spots in films as the Queen, with some of the biggest acting names in the world. She was the total spitting image of the Queen, and was a consummate professional and a very nice lady to boot. When she was all dressed up in her crown and royal regalia, it would be really easy to forget she was a lookalike and the voice wasn't bad either. As a lookalike, nobody I ever met was a more accurate lookalike than Jeanette Charles. She also had lots of really interesting and funny stories about her time pretending to be the Queen for weddings, supermarket openings and the like. If she hasn't already written a book about her time, she should. I bet she has some good stories to tell.

That's the thing about being a lookalike, so many people in my younger days would sometimes get it in their heads that you actually were the person you were a lookalike of. I used to get the impression that, even if they knew you were just a lookalike, they would fool themselves into believing you were the real thing. And people do some really scary shit, especially the birds, and I will tell you a few hairy tales as we go along.

As you have already read there have been quite a few hairy moments. Most of the time, at the good and well organized upmarket events, mostly it's just good fun, lots of free booze, top notch food, and of course, the birds. It's usually the antics of of women and young birds that get you into trouble because the boys and men sometimes get jealous. It's when you attract the attention of the birds who have boyfriends or husbands nearby that matters tend to kick things off and it's usually just when you are relaxing in a pub.

When I have been into a pub somewhere, and when the birds start looking at you, you can guarantee it's not long before some jealous boyfriend wants to punch your lights out. As a youngster I was a bit too naïve and the penny didn't quite drop as to why some bloke always wanted to smack me in the nose. But as I got older and a bit wiser the penny finally fell into place. Now I understand why all the big celebrities have all these bodyguards. People are just so weird and do some really weird stuff. It did get to the stage at one time that I would get a bit unnerved, especially if I was sitting in a place I didn't know. People would stare, or continually walk past trying to see if it was really who they thought it was.

But you don't have to be a celebrity to attract jealously. I once had this mate who was a stunningly good looking kid. He was a young deckhand who I worked with but he was also a real nice kid and we often went chasing the birds together in foreign ports. Always trying to look like Rod Stewart, I would get more than my share and my good-looking ship mate had little trouble either. One day on shore leave my good-looking ship mate rings me up all excited to tell me he has been signed up to be a model by some top-notch model agency after somebody had stopped him the street. Anyway he gets splashed all over his local newspaper with headlines like 'Local boy becomes top model'. Good for him, I thought, and I doubted I would ever see him on a ship's deck again. Well, it didn't end well. A couple of days later and I get another call. This time from my ship mate's mother, and it was not good news. Apparently, my mate had been on a night out and a gang of lads in pub had started a fight and beat him up really badly. His front teeth had been kicked out and his face really badly battered. It transpired he had been getting all the female attention in some pub over his newspaper story and jealousy had done the rest. Some months later I bumped back into him at sea. Apart from a faded scar across his face and two false front teeth he was still a good-looking lad but after his face was scarred, his modelling career never got off the ground and he never heard again from the agency.

What happened to my ship mate made me think hard and I began to understand more why I bumped into so much trouble. I was always on my guard after what happened to my young ship mate.

It took me a long time to learn how things worked. In my time as a Rod Stewart lookalike, I had been punched about three or four times and been beaten badly only once, as I described earlier at that club outside of Mansfield. However, some of the others who had been doing the lookalike game much longer had some scary tales tell. Elvis had been smacked too many times to remember, by both men and women. Clint Eastwood had ended up in accident and emergency twice. Most of it was from low-end guvvy jobs. When I did high-end jobs in London and the south there was never any trouble.

After the problems at Mansfield I gave the guvvy jobs with Elvis Joe a wide berth. I think even he gave up them up after two more hairy events in the Midlands that ended up in hospital visits. Anyway, by this time someone had spragged up Joe to the boss about his off-the-books work and she gave him his marching orders. I didn't see Joe for a few months and he was replaced with this Chinese Elvis of all things. Yes, that's what I said, a Chinese Elvis. I mean, he was a nice bloke but it didn't go down well with the paying customers and before long Elvis Joe was back on the scene.

CHAPTER FOUR

So anyway, here's another little story of the strange behaviour of human beings when they get carried away and think a famous person is in their midst.

I was once sat in this pub in London before I was due to do a party as Rod Stewart. All my hair is styled like Rod's and I'm dressed the part in these tight leopard skin drainpipes and a multi-colored stripey jacket. Anyway, I had some time to kill and got bored in my hotel room so I foolishly thought I'd have a swift pint whilst waiting for my taxi. So I'm sat in this London pub having a moment to myself and minding my own business waiting for a cab to pick me up and take me to this rich posh wedding hoe-down being held at Claridges hotel, and you don't get much posher than that do you. I should have known what was coming being from Hull but when you are young bad stuff happening is the furthest from your mind and I am off my guard.

At the time I hadn't been doing the lookalike game long, and so I was a bit green about how odd people could behave. Anyway, I could see all these birds looking at me and whispering. Admittedly, I was enjoying the attention but I was also getting a few fierce glares of the 'death awaits you' variety off their boyfriends. I had the feeling, as the newspapers often say, a 'scuffle' was about to break out. I'm getting a bit wary now. I don't want any trouble as I am fully togged up in my Rod Stewart gear and the last thing I need is turning up to this wedding reception with a black eye, fat lip and cauliflower ear with my clothes torn to shreds. So I turn my back on this staring horde of girls and these barbarians hoping I would attract less attention. Alas things did not turn out as planned and all turning my back did was to increase the curiosity of the girls, especially as I started hearing girly giggles of: "It is him! It's him I tell you! It's Rod Stewart!"

"Oh fuck," I thought. "Why hadn't I decided to just stay in the hotel room next door and wait for the taxi?"

Anyway, so the landlord was a few feet away wiping down the tables and I could see him staring, seemingly racking his brains over who I was. I was hoping the penny wouldn't drop before my taxi arrived but the landlord's stares are getting more intense, and then clunk! The penny does drop and suddenly he starts to laugh and is pointing at me, "It's you, innit?" he says at me. I smile awkwardly and he's across the room like a crossbow bolt staring down at me. "It's bleedin' Rod Stewart, bleedin 'ell!!!" and he shouts across to the barmaid: "Eh Betty, it's Rod Stewart!"

By now all the pub was looking, and I was beginning to wish the earth would open and swallow me up. "Eh, what ya drinking Rod?" the landlord says to me. "On the house! If ya fancy a meat pie and mushy peas, it's on the house whatever ya like!"

Now I'm not a one to look a gift horse in the mouth and freebies are usually part of the perks the real Rod Stewart no doubt gets in great abundance - not sure about meat pie and mushy peas, though, I'll have to ask Rod next time I see him.

I've had many free drinks bought and many free meals at restaurants and, of course, some of the best free shags going. Yes, being a Rod Stewart lookalike, the shag was on tap and top totty to boot. You name the place and I've banged them in it, under dining tables, inside bogs, on car bonnets, in bushes. Too many places to remember in fact. I recall one month I was banging so many birds, that I was getting friction burns and blisters on my bell end and ended up seeing the knob doctor. "You've got a badly swollen penal helmet, "he informed me. "Just try keeping it in your pants, and giving it a few days of rest and recuperation."

"Well, thanks Doc," I replied and duly rubbed on the prescribed cream twice a day. Within a week my knob end was fighting fit and ready for action again.

I did try to tone down the birds for a while, I swear I really did, but you have to remember I was only young and once I had got a few down me, it has hard to stop. When I got a hot wet snog with tongue down the throat and with an urgent female box pressing on the old pork truncheon, I just couldn't resist the temptation. The next I knew I would be on the floor somewhere under the table slamming in the lamb, as they say. Ask yourself, who would pass up freebies whether it's beer, stuff, or a shag with a sexy bird? Nobody that's who. It was just a perk of the job and really all I was doing was picking up Rod Stewart's leftovers, sort of. As far as freebies were concerned, I mean Rod Stewart is rich after all, and doesn't really need them but me ? I'm just a humble merchant seaman, so my apologies to Rod and since the landlord had offered, I bummed a double vodka and lime out of him – on the house, of course. I passed on the meat pie and mushy peas offer as the latter tend to go through me and one wet fart and you've got more than you bargained for in your underpants.

Next thing I knew and this fussing landlord's wife is down with a camera and I'm posing, first with the landlord, then his wife, then the barmaid is in on the act rubbing her thigh all over my leg. If I had had the time I'd have slipped her one because although she was older than me, she was a sexy-looking boiler with these big thick, stocking-covered, riding thighs. Soon there's a queue of birds waiting for my autograph and sat in the corner spitting blood, fire and snot are all of their blokes.

By now, these birds were all half drunk and asking me for kisses. They're plonking great wet open mouth, stonking tongue down the throat, tonsil-tickling groan-gripper jobs on my mouth, one after the other with some of them sucking on me like sink plunger, and others pressing their boxes all over my groin in full view of their Viking lookalike boyfriends. I am mentally pleading by now for my taxi to turn up and rescue me, and from the corner of my eye, I see this big fat bird grab a full pint pot of beer from a table, and she is walking purposely towards me like a sauntering Hull FC rugby prop forward. She has this look on her face that tells me what she's going to do with the pint. Suddenly this fat bird is shouting across the pub: "Fucking Rod Stewart, what an ugly bastard!!!" I can see she is about to launch this pint at me but I skilfully duck and the liquid flies over my head and sloshes straight into the face of the landlord and the landlady. They are sodden right through, from head to foot, in best bitter. So then the shit starts flying with a vengeance. This fat bird suddenly stops in her tracks as she realizes what she has done and what is coming in her direction. The landlord just glares at her like a volcano about to explode and then he does explode just like Krakatoa. Without even a pause to consider this bird was a women of sorts, in one smooth instant moment of reflex the landlord throws this massive right hook at the fat bird. It solidly connects with a dull thud and this fat bird goes travelling at some speed of knots across a table, her legs going up in the air, as she gives a sorry flash of her gusset as she goes. She lands with a crash on the floor with glasses smashing around her on the floor creating a flood of spilled beer. She is out cold in the land of nod, with blood streaming out of her nose. "Oh fuck!" I thought.

Now I take one look at these blokes starting to come off their seats, and I get a very bad feeling about future imminent developments and, in particular, my health. Suddenly pint pots of beer are flying in all directions across the pub, and I dive for cover under a nearby table with mayhem breaking out all around me. All I can hear is banging, crashing and the thuds and cracks of punches and kicks landing, intermingled with loud obscenities.

From under the table, I crawl commando-style towards the door with punches still being swung in all directions. As I make it to the door at ground level, it suddenly opens and I'm staring at a pair of shiny black shoes. I look slowly upwards and see a black cab is stood waiting outside with the driver stood in the pub doorway watching this mass riot. Not being brave in situations like this and concerned I was about to get my face rearranged, I bolted for the safety and sanctuary of his cab. We drove away with me panting thankfully at my near miss. The taxi driver was laughing, "I take it they don't like Rod Stewart in there then," he said sniggering sarcastically.

"Yeah," I said, "I think you could say that."

So that's just one of many little episodes I had as my time as a Rod lookalike but there's more to come and they are certainly interesting. I am now 62 years old and retired from the merchant navy but have loads of fantastic memories to look back thanks to Sir Rod.

CHAPTER FIVE

But for now, if I just can take you back to the beginning of the book and back to the reality of that hotel room in the 1970s where it all started after a Rod Stewart lookalike party and my big fuck-off hangover. Remember?

Now you would be amazed at what rich people with more money than they know what to do with will pay you to appear at their parties and social gatherings or to open pubs and discos. From what I can remember of this particular night's little rich shindig is that it was some millionaire's daughter getting married so it was no expense spared with nothing too much trouble to ensure a thumping expensive marital send-off. They had paid for me to take a taxi from Hull to this big posh house in its own grounds in Knightsbridge. I didn't go to wedding or anything but along with Marilyn Monroe, Elvis Presley, Cary Grant, Elizabeth Taylor, Audrey Hepburn and a young Jim Reeves lookalike who I thought looked more like Vic Reeves, we all piled into the reception that was being held in this big banquet-style room at the Grosvenor House Hotel in Park Lane. Naturally, the free booze was flowing like water and a very top-notch all-you-can-eat sit down dinner and buffet was being served. Afterwards, as usual, things warmed up as the dinner turned into a disco and party went on late into the evening with everybody,

including us lookalikes, dancing and drinking the night
away.

Coming from a northern backwater like Hull, it was eye-
opener to see how the other half lived. What this wedding
cost would have kept the whole of Hessle Road in Hull
where I lived in grub for year.

By now, I was getting regular work as a Rod Stewart
lookalike when I was home from sea and the money was
just so good. This was 1973 and for just for a day's work as
a lookalike I could clear three to five hundred smackers
plus expenses straight in my arsehole back pocket and all
tax free. I mean, as a merchant seaman deck officer in
those days I was lucky to clear £29 quid a week, let alone a
day. So this was big, big money for me.

The jobs were coming in from both the agency and quite a
lot of odd guvvy jobs via my mate Joe, the Elvis lookalike,
who was arranging work behind the agency's back. These
guvvy jobs were also good money and they could make us
around twenty or thirty quid more each time we did one.
That was a lot of money in those days and not to be sniffed
at by any means. You're talking quite a few grand in
today's money at least, if not more so it was difficult to
turn down. I did feel a bit guilty I was double-crossing the
agency who had started all this Rod Stewart lookalike
business in the first place but once I got the guvvy money
in my hand any feelings of guilt didn't last long. Aside from
the money, there were the irresistible added benefits of
the birds and they came in all shapes, sizes, rich, mega rich
and poor.

The birds would always want their picture taken with you
and one thing would usually lead to another. The posh
birds especially would always drop their knickers and

throw in a free bonk. As I said earlier, you name the place and I've had a bonk in it.

One time after this big posh wedding shindig at a big knob's country house I got off with this right rich young nymphomaniac. I spent the evening with this gorgeous millionaire's daughter banging away into the midnight hours in these stables with a hay loft overhead. To look at the angelic face of this rich Daddy's girl, you would think butter would not have melted in her mouth, especially if Daddy was around.

When all us lookalikes arrived at this wedding party, posh-talking Daddy came across and introduced all his family, and of course we got the usual patronizing smiles, along with a "make sure you watch the silver" type of attitude. Being from Hull, as soon as they heard my accent, it was more like "hide the family silver" but I just let it go over my head.

I could see this posh bloke's daughter was taken with me, and she insisted on getting a photograph with my arm around her. Anyway, after the cameraman snapped his shot she leaned over and gave me a peck on the cheek and suddenly squeezed my tackle. Then she grabs my hand and leads me into this study just off this massive Tudor-type hallway. She then starts smothering me in big wet, open-mouth kisses with her tongue tickling my tonsils. Although she's wearing this elaborate and awkward ball gown, she's pressing her lips onto mine and lifting the front of her skirt and she has no tights on. She just pulls her small brief knickers aside, takes me in her hand, slides me in and we end up ramming each other off the wall for fifteen minutes. After we have both shot our bolts, she's all hot, bothered and panting and says: "I'll just put in an appearance and meet you outside in ten minutes. You had better be there, or Daddy will get to hear of it." Then she pecks me on the lips and says in one very long hot posh breath: "I badly need finishing off."

I took the Daddy part to be a warning to meet her outside or else, not that I needed it since I badly needed finishing off too.

So having pulled up my pants off I toddle back into party, and things are hotting up big time there too as the booze is flowing like water and couples are snogging all over the place. Even posh little Daddy is in a darkened corner snogging the lips off some young drunk bird with his hand up her skirt before they suddenly both slide out the door and into a side room. The whole party is descending into a Roman orgy and I see my mate Alvin Stardust slide under the banqueting table with some bird and he is gone. I go to the bar and my glass is filled with what I know not and I down it in one. Again my glass is automatically filled and by now I'm throwing them down my neck and well on my way to La La Land. By this time two young drunk birds have hold of me, one is snogging me with the other trying to get her hand down my pants. I'm so drunk that I'm not sure where I am and I've totally forgotten about meeting my rich young nymphomaniac outside. By now she is back inside and pushing these two girls off me like a greedy hyena fighting over a carcass. She drags me outside by the hand, rushes me across this courtyard and into these dark stables, almost ordering me to climb the hayloft ladders. Now I was in no fit state to climb stairs never mind a ladder in the dark but she shoved me urgently towards the ladders and with her behind me pushed my arse upwards and launched me like a rocket into the hayloft. She dragged me behind a pile of hay and we rolled about kissing and riving at each other, with bits of clothing being thrown off in all directions. Now I was totally and absolutely out of the game and pissed to the eyeballs with my head spinning in this darkened hayloft. However I wasn't so drunk I was going to miss climbing aboard this bird and I was still gagging for it as she was. The thing about being drunk but not too drunk is that you can bonk as hard as you like but nothing happens and you can go on almost forever. I must have been on her for a couple hours and still couldn't get there but she was loving it and totally insatiable. I had her in a knee trembler against a haystack, next doggy, sideways, with her on top and reversed on top. Yes, we went through the Karma Sutra from page one to the end and back again. I have never been ragged like that by a bird in all my life. I don't remember much after that apart from things going even darker before we both fell asleep. We must have been so pissed we slept in the hayloft and woke up the next day sometime in the afternoon, still half naked and both with a hazy memory of recent events.

As was becoming far too usual, I had a massive hangover and was dying for a piss with a full on morning glory hard on even though it was mid-afternoon. Before I could say Jack Flash, this bird looks me, smacks this big wet open mouth kiss on me and says: "Never waste a hard-on, that's my motto, big boy!" This bird just jumps astride my dick, and rides me like she is riding her prize stallion for half an hour, screaming at the top her voice like a banshee. It transpired after we both dusted the hay off our clothes and got dressed and crept back to this big house, everybody had evaporated and the place was totally empty. By now I was half sober and it was daylight. It was only then that I could appreciate the massive size of the property. The whole house was still a mess from the night before but it was absolutely deserted. "Where has everybody gone?" I said.

"Oh, don't worry about them," she says half smiling, "By this time my big sister will be on her way to Florence for her honeymoon and looking forward to some serious cock. My sister has always likes her cock."

Yes, I thought silently to myself, as does her little sister. "And what about Daddy?" I said mocking a posh voice.

"Oh don't worry about him," she answered smiling, "He'll be gone for days. Daddy still has a penchant for the young tight girly ones. He's a bit of an old perv really, but he's still a good brick."

I had no idea what a 'brick' was apart from the type in a wall. I gleaned it was some posh word for a dirty old man. Now being a plain young and naïve Hull lad, this world was all new to me and real eye-opener on how the other half lived. I was curious. "Dun't ya' Mam know what Pop's getting up to then, banging these young lasses?" Now how naïve is that question?

"Well of course she does," she answered obviously. "But dun't she mind?" I asked.

My young lady sort of smiled back at my naivety. "Oh dear," she said, "You certainly are very provincial. Mummy is kept well-oiled with the 19-year-old gardener." Again there was a language difficulty here and stuff was getting lost in translation. I had no idea what 'provincial' meant so I looked at her and she looked back at me and we both burst out laughing. She took my hand and, giggling, she mischievously led me back upstairs for round three, or was it four? Anyway, who cares? I was losing count and was so very young back then. This girl just turned me on. God did she turn me on or what? She was posh, absolutely

beautiful, such fun to be with and God was she good in the sack. It was like riding a bucking bronco for an hour.
I wasn't too sure of what to make of her. I mean, where I come from she would have been called the local bike, a bit of a slag. But she made it seem all seem so normal and that dropping your knickers was just a recreational activity with sex to be enjoyed at every opportunity. And who was I to argue? I was getting my end away with a gorgeous bird and getting paid for it. I decided to lay back and just go with the flow. I knew after all, this would seem like a dream in a few days, when I would be back on board some rust bucket ship, with a rough arse crew of grunts and sailing to I don't don't where. I would stay in this dream as long as I could. The only annoying habit she had was that as we were slamming away, she would cry out in throes of passion: "Fuck me Rod, fuck me Rod." It would have been nice if she wanted to shag me for me. But you can't have everything can you?

So for the next few days I spent most of my time drinking left over champagne and banging away with this bird in this big fuck-off four poster bed till the cock crowed. In between shagging, this bed had a pop-up TV and a bedside drinks cabinet. We would lay silently, watch telly, dipping into the drinks cabinet until just tipsy and slowly kiss and kiss. Either she would climb on top of me or I would climb on top of her and we would slowly grind each other into the bed and make it last for hours.
They were a few lost days, and sadly it was a long, long time ago. I tell you, I could have easily have fallen in love with this posh bird and the money that went with her but I think Daddy would have had something to say about his daughter hooking with a bit of rough stuff from Hull.

And as ever, nothing lasts does it? When you are enjoying yourself time moves so quickly so we kissed a long good bye on the drive. It was a long, very long and passionate kiss, "Call me when you're back in port, my little Rod Stewart," she said with just the hint of a sad whisper. "I will, I promise," I answered in-between sultry hot breaths. I could feel a rising in my pants but I knew I would have to go to catch my ship. I did manage to tear myself away and a taxi waiting on the drive took me back to my hotel to pick up my suitcase, my seaman's card and passport and I was whisked off to Heathrow Airport where I was due to catch a plane to Saudi Arabia and then to Iran and a boat ride to Kharg Island oil terminal to pick up my ship.

I still felt a bit rough by the time I reached Heathrow Airport but as walked through check-in I caught a glimpse of myself in a nearby mirror and didn't look half as bad as I felt, even if I say so myself. God, was I a big-headed bastard in those days or what? Of course, I was still very young and full of myself so why not? After all, I was Rod Stewart - or the next best thing to the real McCoy. Well, it works for me anyway.

I was still in my Rod Stewart gear and getting the usual looks with birds stopping me for autographs, a kiss and cuddle and some photographs. I dumped my baggage at the check-in desk and met up with some of the crew catching the same flight. Many of us knew each other, and a couple of guys were from Hull as I remember. So we made our way through security and into duty free to wait for our flight to be called. We made straight for this massive bar lounge in duty free, and we are all talking over past sea trips and exchanging stories, and suddenly I get this tap on my shoulder. I turn round and this really

well-dressed bloke is standing there smiling, and he says:
"My mate thinks you are taking the piss."
"What you talking about mate?" I said back at him
aggressively.
"My mate over there," and he pointed at this bloke, who
waved.
And fuck me it was Rod Stewart himself, who was sat
down and beckoning me over. How could I resist? So this
bloke led me across, and a laughing Rod Stewart asked me
sit down. "Are you taking the piss or what?" he asked me.
I thought I'd poke back. "It's not me taking the piss, it's
you," I said smiling. So anyway I sat down and we got
talking and I watched as the crew at the bar watched with
mouths gawping open.
"What you drinking?" asked Rod Stewart.
"I can't take a drink without my mates," I said, trying it on
with a sly smile, and with that, Rod Stewart bought the
whole crew a drink. A few minutes later and the real Rod
Stewart was on his feet as they called his flight. He shook
my hand and was gone with a smile.
My mates never stopped talking about it for months. I
tried not to wash my hand for a week after shaking his
hand. Whatever you hear about Rod Stewart, all I can say
is what a fantastic bloke he is. Totally down to earth and
totally not drunk on his own self-importance. One of the
world's truly nice people. I have to say I was shocked at
how nice he was and how he took my imitation of him in
such a good way. I thought he might take offence. My only
criticism was that he didn't put a few quid behind the bar
for me and the crew as we had a few hours to wait for our
flight but I'll be content with just meeting my lifetime
hero.

CHAPTER SIX

Before catching our flight, we all settled down in the duty free lounge and, as merchant seaman do, we chucked the beer down our neck until our departure number was called. We boarded the plane all half pissed, and I was so shagged out from my last few days with the posh bird that I soon fell asleep after fastening my seat belt. I have to admit that I did dream about her and thought about her for many days and nights when I was laid in a lonely cabin in the middle of some endless boring ocean.

We did exchange letters for a few months and one time, as good as my word, I called her and I met her in Trafalgar Square in London during a spell ashore. She paid for us to have a three-day stop at the posh and very expensive Charring Cross Hotel so I spent the next 72 hours being totally spoilt rotten, drinking in our room and shagging from dusk till dawn. It was a bit of an unreal time for me. I was from the backwater town of Hull and this posh bird, who shall remain nameless, was from the rich Chelsea set. It was like I was living in an alternative reality. Even when she told me she was getting married but that we could still meet it didn't shock me. That seemed to be her world, a rich world of pretence and sham marriages of convenience for position. To me, the world she lived in seemed like a charade. "You're getting married?" I said with a note of animated outrage. "You'll have a husband to keep you well satisfied in the bedroom."

"It doesn't work like you think in my world," she said looking at me forlornly. "Marriage is more about appearances and making alliances. It's what's expected of me. Jeremy's family is an old one, as is mine."

"You mean you don't love this bloke then?" I replied.

Now you have to understand me. In the world I come from, you usually marry a bird because you are in love or you have got her up the duff and, as a result, Daddy and her brothers are going to smash your head in if you don't do the decent thing. This getting married for money and position lark, I just didn't get. I mean it wasn't as though this bird came from a poor family. She seemed stinking rich to me. But I guess, as I have got older and wiser, I have learned that money, like shit, sticks together.

"Oh Terry," she answered back cynically, "You are such an old romantic. Jeremy is more likely to fancy you than me."

"What, you mean he's a woofta!" I said aloud (apologies for using the 'woofta' word but's it's the 1970s here). "What the 'ell you marrying him for then?"

"Because it will make my Daddy happy and his parents will thank God he isn't, as you say so quaintly say, a woofta, as they know he is. And once married, I will go my way and Jeremy will go his and when his parents have departed their mortal coil I'll get a nice quiet amicable divorce and I'll get a nice settlement and we'll both live happily ever after. Jeremy will ride off into the sunset with Bernard and I'll have you."

"You've got this all worked out, haven't you?" I said slightly astounded.

In this little plan of hers, I suspected I would be the lifelong 'bit of rough on side' and provide the cock as a kept man. But no matter how much I enjoyed being in her knickers, I still had a bit of good old-fashioned working class morality left in me. Somehow, this bed-hopping and pretence just didn't seem right me. Now I'm not moralizing or anything but as my old gran would say: "It's a bit of a going on, isn't it?" And while I was enjoying my time with this bird, all this bohemian lifestyle stuff was a bit over my head. And in any case, I had women troubles of my own back in Hull. Now did I say I was perfect?

To cut a very long story short, while I liked this posh bird and the sex was hot as hell we came from totally different worlds and a long-term relationship really had disaster written all over it. It would have never worked in a million years. I mean I was tempted and I was having all these mercenary money thoughts because she was very rich but I snapped out of it.

Anyway, eventually me and this posh bird did go our separate ways.

For about a year I seemed to be always flying out of Heathrow Airport meeting some ship somewhere in the world or maybe doing some Rod Stewart lookalike party. I would fit a few days in with my posh bird that usually ended up at the Charring Cross Hotel spending all our time on horizontal hold in bed and shagging till the cows came home. Eventually it fizzled out and I met her once more after she had married this Jeremy bloke. She would cry on my shoulder telling me how unhappy she was and I would pretend to hold her tightly and understand while rolling my eyes behind her back. It was all getting a bit too pathetic for me. To be brutal, I was bored with her and her constant moaning was pissing me of. Well, she had made her bed and, as me old Mum would have said: "Now she has to lie on it."

By this time my fascination with her had worn a bit thin, and her endless little spoilt rich bird whining was becoming just a bit tiresome. I knew a thousand people in Hull where I came from who would have given their eye teeth to have her money and cushy lifestyle. But life's all relative I suppose. I doubt she knew the meaning of a hard day's work or even suspected the impoverished world I came from actually existed. Somehow I just couldn't see her, sat on the couch with my mum dunking digestive biscuits and watching Coronation Street. It was a princess and pauper job. I will though give her one thing, she wasn't snob. If we were out and about around London and bumped into her posh friends, she would always introduce me and say we were an item. I did go to many posh West End parties with her, met many famous people and lots of rich ones too. We had a good time but I knew I was getting in too deep when she told me she was in love in with me. I was totally confused by then. I had total mixed feelings. I didn't belong in her world and she didn't belong in mine. She now wanted more from me than I wanted give, and I just couldn't see myself fitting into her world or her into mine. My parents lived in a council house in Hull, and her parents were titled, I won't say what. I suppose the bottom line was that I felt a little inferior. All her young hot friends were high flying, in banking and such like. I just had nothing in common with them. Whichever way I looked at it, I just couldn't see it working.

So with her little rich girl bleating, whining and complaining, I had enough, I decided it was time to jump ship. To borrow a much used Hull phrase, I blew her out and I just didn't ring her anymore. Since she had no way of contacting me that was that. Another episode was over but they were interesting days. Looking back, the old days always do seem more interesting and I often wonder what happened to her and what she looks like now. I sometimes sit quietly in my little two-up two down house at the ripe old age of 62 while our lass is doing the ironing and can't help wonder how different things might have been. Memories at our time life can be a real pain in the arse.

I suppose at this stage I might as well make another admission, if I'm going to be honest. There was just one other little added complication to my life at this point. While I was involved with this London posh bird, I was like having other bird troubles at home in Hull. I might as well admit it, yes, at that time my love life was getting more complicated by the minute, as I had a regular girlfriend in Hull, who I always promised myself I would stay faithful to - usually after I had climbed out of bed with some other bird. I know I keep blaming this, but I'll say it again, I was young back then and my loins always seemed to be bulging and I was cashing in on fanny on tap as Rod Stewart so I just couldn't keep it in my pants. I always started out with the best intentions towards my girlfriend in Hull, but sometimes I could be at sea for weeks and pulling your plonker only works for a short time until you need to bang it in the real thing. I'm sure any of the lads reading this will know what I mean, especially any merchant seaman out there. I am but flesh and blood after all. At least my intentions, if not my actions, were honorable towards my regular girlfriend in Hull. To prove it, we did get engaged at one time but amid a burst of emotional tears she ended up smacking me one in the mouth and throwing my engagement ring in my face after accusing me of shagging her sister.

As for the other whisper going around at that time, there was absolutely no evidence I had also shagged her mother. Malicious rumours spread quickly in small towns like Hull and I found I needed to keep my head down for a few months as the word was certain people were looking for me. So it was off back to sea and a very long contract in the hope that by the time I got back memories would be short. I would just add here that when this older woman chatted me up in Hull because she liked Rod Stewart, I had absolutely no idea it was my girlfriend's sister. As for shagging the mother, let's just say I am taking the fifth on that one.

Birds were just one of many benefits of looking like Rod Stewart, you had some of the most beautiful birds on tap and just throwing themselves at you. I mean I just looked like Rod Stewart. I imagine the real Rod must have been banging them out ten to the dozen, I was just getting his 'wanna-shag' Rod Stewart left overs. But don't get me wrong if you are reading this Rod, I have a lot to thank you for, not least quite a few trips to the knob doctor. Yes, if I had one downfall in my Rod Stewart lookalike days, it was the birds. I just couldn't keep out of their knickers once the offer had had been thrown at me. I suppose I had become a bit of a sexaholic.

CHAPTER SEVEN

One time I was taking this plane out of Heathrow Airport to catch a ship in Japan and had been about fifteen minutes in the air and the seat belt signs are off. I was flying Japan Airlines and I could see this gorgeous Japanese air stewardess looking at me along with a few other passengers who were giving me knowing looks and continuously staring like they were racking their brains. Now this stewardess was hot and I mean hot. She had curves so teasing I could feel a throbbing and gagging in my groin. Her uniform fitted her like tight snakeskin over her nubile little body, and oh my God, when she bent down I could not take my eyes off her tight little skirt and the skimpy outline of her little knickers on her tight rabbit bum. It was enough to get me almost ready to cream one off in the bog.

Anyway, I was snatching a sneaky stare at her and she is doing the same to me. I can see her looking over again and again in my direction and I knew, I just knew I would be tearing off her knickers and sliding into oriental paradise in the not too distant future. I had never shagged a Japanese bird before and was mentally torturing myself just thinking about slipping between her legs, in the nicest possible way you understand. Like most men, uniforms to do it for me, they really do ring my bells. "Ding, dong!" as Leslie Phillips used to say.

So I'm seated in economy in the middle of this plane, almost having a wet dream about this Japanese air hostess who comes to serve me first with the drinks trolley, much to the disgust of the other passengers. And why not? After all, I am Rod Stewart, aren't I?

So anyway, I was about push my Rod Stewart angle to the extreme so I could to get into this Jap bird's knickers. From the signals I was getting from her I knew she was gagging for me as much as I was gagging for her. So as she comes up to my seat, I get this big pouting wide, white toothy smile, and she asks me what I would like to drink in this cute squeaky, broken English Japanese voice. She was so close by now she was pressing the inner part of her thigh against my hand that was resting on the arm rest and I automatically stroked my hand up her inside thigh through the split in her skirt. She let my hand stroke up the inside of her leg to the top, and I quickly squeezed her crutch, and she let out a heavy breath, closed her eyes for a second and slightly lurched towards my hand. She stared right into my eyes and we exchanged 'eye talk'. Anyway, I ordered a vodka and orange and my hand discreetly fell away as she reluctantly moved to get my drink. So she hands me a plastic glass and pours in the vodka and just as she pours the orange from this big jug flask, she seems to trip and spills the lot in my lap and I'm soaked right through to my skiddies.

"Oh, oh, I so sorry!" she panics in this squeaky Japanese voice, and the next thing I know she is pulling me up out my seat, "You come, come with me, and I dry you." By now she has taken my hand and is almost pulling me down the aisle and behind the curtains, and she leaves me standing next to the bog, "You stay here I get you towel and trousers," she says with this big smile and cute squeaky voice I am now so taken with, "Steward always have spare pair. You wait, I be back." A minute later and she is back carrying a spare pair of Japanese Airline trousers and a towel. She suddenly opens the bog door and pushes me inside, and then cheekily follows me in and slams the door shut, and suddenly locks the door. And suddenly she is glaring at me with these wild black eyes and in this hot breath Japanese accent spurts out: "Rod Stewart! We do big fucky, fucky now!" It didn't sound much like a request and she flung herself on me, and next her face was stuck on mine and we were swapping deep tongues, and before you can say Jack Flash, I have her skirt up around her waist, and she is pulling down my zipper and then my pants and she starts sliding her hands all over my thighs and groin. Needless to say, I'm as stiff as a flag polein a flash. By now she was almost like an alley cat on heat, and she pushed me backwards onto the bog seat. The cold bog seat was a shock to my bare arse, I can tell you. By now both my pants and underpants are around my ankles and she is sucking on me like there is no tomorrow while at the same time smoothly sliding off her off her tights and knickers. The next I know she straddles across me on the bog seat, takes my knob and guides me skillfully inside, and she is bouncing up and down on me and going for it hammer and tongs. By this time we have some turbulence, and as the plane judders through it's not like we are having to work at this at all. We ended bonking like jack rabbits bouncing around this aircraft bog with turbulence throwing us all over the place. The next minute I have her tight little arse balanced on the sink, with her legs round my waist, and I am banging at her like a jack hammer. We bonk away for half an hour with her screaming like a banshee, while passengers outside thump on the bog door at 32,000 feet wondering what the hell is going on inside. I think in our throes of animal urgency, we had both lost any sense of decency by then and cared little who heard us, or who was waiting outside to use the bog. So by this time we are both going for it and we are slamming into each other, and the sink is almost coming off the wall, and then suddenly we are both there and both, steaming hot, sweating and exhausted. The urgency had gone in both of us, and we both started to quickly straighten our clothes, getting ready to face those waiting outside. By the time we emerged, she had pulled her skimpy knickers up, straightened her uniform and I was wearing these baggy ill-fitting Japanese Airways trousers. We both sort of emerged a little abashed and dashed out into the waiting queue outside all red-faced while people stared at us with knowing smiles. I felt like I wanted the earth to swallow me but as I sheepishly took my seat I suddenly got this round of loud applause and cheering as I sat down. My face was glowing red with embarrassment while the air hostess just scurried into the back of the plane and kept a low profile for the rest of the flight. Eventually, I fell asleep after pigging out on the free inflight booze.

So yes, thanks to having a mush like Rod Stewart, I was now a fully-fledged member of the mile-high club and would in the future get the same treatment on British Airways, Lufthansa and Air France.

Later this Japanese stewardess pushed her hotel name and room number into my hand as I'm getting off the plane as pissed as a fart having consumed as many inflight freebies as I could.

As luck would have it, she was laying over in Tokyo for three days and I didn't have to get my ship for two days so we spent two days bunked up in her room. Downstairs in the hotel lounge me and this stewardess would get free drinks all night from other customers, who thought they were buying drinks for Rod Stewart. I would do my stuff, signing autographs and posing for pictures. I was selling myself like one of those sea side monkeys you have your picture taken with on the Blackpool sea front but who cares? I certainly didn't. I was having the time of my life and loving every minute of it.

Karaoke has always been big in Japan before it ever got to the UK. In Japanese bars and hotels there was always a microphone and drunken people would just saunter up to the microphone and just start crowing out a song. Whether they could sing or not, nobody really took any notice. It was just part of the culture. Well, it wasn't long before the hotel manager was up and on the microphone, and although I had no idea what he was talking about, he was pointing to me in this crowded hotel lounge and people just started clapping. Next he was waving me to come forward. I was baffled but my little Japanese girl friend said: "He wants you to come up and sing Rod." I don't know why she kept calling me Rod as by now she knew I was not the real Rod Stewart, but it didn't stop her. But she just kept on saying, "No, no, you Rod Stewart. Look no-one cares, they think you Rod Stewart."

So I just shrugged my shoulders and gave up denying it in the end. I mean that's the type of mentality I met all the time. They really knew I wasn't Rod Stewart, but they just wanted me to be him. So who was I to shatter their illusion, and they wanted to spoil me because of it. Who was I to argue?

Now, while I might look like Rod Stewart I certainly don't sound like Rod Stewart and cannot sing like him either. In fact, I sound more like Kermit the Frog whenever I tried to sing like Rod Stewart. I would only chance singing if I had had a few drinks down my neck and a bit of Dutch courage. However, experience told me, once I got up there and started blasting out a Rod Stewart, and sounding more like I had a chronic sore throat, no one cared that I was awful. They were just taken by the moment and, usually like me, were just so full of booze that no one cared any way. We were just having a good time. No-one was harmed and that was good enough for me.

Everyone in the hotel lounge was now on their feet and egging me to go up and sing. My new Japanese girlfriend was now pushing me forward and really I had no choice. So I'm now standing on this small stage with hundreds of hotel guests looking at me, and cameras are flashing all over the place, and the hotel manager pushes the microphone into my hand and I get a big round of applause. The strains of Maggie May start playing but I don't know all the words and those on the screen in front of me are in Japanese. Anyway, fuck it, I just go for it and the parts I don't know I just, like mumble. Surprisingly, it's working. The crowd don't give a fuck that I can't sing and are going mad. Some are even dancing and as the music fades, a big cheer goes up and I'm being mobbed. Every man and his dog wants their picture taken with me and to buy me a drink. I even did autographs. I have to admit I signed them Rod Stewart but the posing for photographs with Rod Stewart fans just went on and on. After an hour and I managed to retreat back to my table and the free drinks on my table are piling up. By the end of the night I am totally wasted and the hotel manager comes across, to me. "You stay here long time, all free," he says, "And I pay you good." He pushes a wad of Japanese Yen in my hand. It turned out to be worth about £300 UK sterling.

I explain via my Japanese girlfriend that I have to fly to Los Angeles in a couple days for a concert (Was I now lying or what?) but could squeeze in another night and would then have to be off. By now I had got some confidence and they really didn't care if I couldn't sing like Rod Stewart or not and I just blagged it, getting another wad of Japanese cash the next night for my troubles and all the free booze I could drink. I was now a few hundred quid up in Yen and sorely tempted to miss my ship. I knew if I did, it was likely that I would not only end up being deported from Japan as an illegal alien, but also blacklisted at the UK shipping office. So I quickly put that one out my head.

This Japanese bird spoke quite good English, and although I'm sure she really knew I was not the real Rod Stewart, she had her "moment with Rod" and we spent our two days, and two long nights together with her crying out in "Oh fuck me Rod, fuck me hard," when we got down to business. Occasionally, she would indulge in some sultry Japanese screaming as she rode me to exhaustion. With the benefit of looking like Rod Stewart, you have to forgive me for pigging out on the pro bono sex with this gorgeous, tight nubile bird. Who cared if she wanted me to be Rod Stewart? I just played along with our little pretense and filled my boots up to the gunnels. Two days later, with the pair of us knackered, we kissed goodbye after another long passionate night, and she caught her flight and I caught my ship. I also had a hot wad of Japanese cash burning a hole in my pocket for my troubles. (Bloody hell I'm exhausted just writing this. And as I write, it is so strange, and incredible to think this event was well over 40 years. Oh how the years of youth fly by and now I have trouble raising a smile.)

CHAPTER EIGHT

Now I hope you remember that whilst I'm telling you these stories, I'm still in the hotel back in the 1970s with a big hangover after a lookalike gig with all my lookalike mates. I do keep getting carried away, don't I ?

Oh well, if you're not impressed please yourself but it does make life interesting, very interesting in fact, especially with the ladies on foreign shores, but I'll get to that later, after I have got over this big fuck off hangover. Now remember, we are back in the hotel where this book started and we can't go on with you readers getting lost can we?

I'm in the bathroom and still have a frazzled brain. I'm still sitting on the toilet with my guts bubbling and feeling as rough as arseholes.
"What time is it," I groaned at my mate Elvis.
Elvis offers me his wrist because he cannot focus his eyes as he is still half-pissed. "Half ten, thank God for that," I moaned to myself.
I had a plane to catch at Heathrow at one o'clock as I was flying out to Canada to catch my ship. It was a container ship and it was likely I would not see the shores of the UK for some time. Despite that, I loved my job, wouldn't change it for anything.

Coming from Hull I was brought up on Hessle Road, a big sea-going community as it was then in the 1960s and 1970s. It's gone to rat shit now but that's another story. Anyway, the sea was in my family's' blood. My Dad went to sea, some of my elder brothers and nearly all my mates were in the merchant navy "big boating" or on deep sea trawlers. I did a stint on trawlers to get my time in and then went "big boating". "Big boating" is just a slang term for the merchant navy as opposed to working on trawlers. It was all I ever wanted to do since I was little.

I'll paint the picture of my life as we go along but on my travels I have to admit that I played the Rod Stewart card whenever I could.

But just for the moment, let's get back to reality of where this book starts and the hotel room, and this big bleedin' hangover I've got and all I want to do at this moment is try and feel like a living, breathing human being again.

"Bloody 'ell," says my mate Elvis grinning. He's still laid in the bath and wafting his hand at the stink I'd left floating in the bathroom after dropping my guts, "Something must've crawled up you and died. Open the bloody window will you."

"Better out than in, mate," I said back.

"Not from where I am," said Elvis. "And you, ya dirty little tow rag, you were going at it hammer and tongs last night weren't you?"

"What do you mean?" I asked back quickly, "I didn't make a prat of myself did I? I can't remember a thing."

"So you don't remember that little redhead with the tight rat arse you disappeared with upstairs with?" said Elvis with a mischievous smile, "She was all over you like a rash at the reception."

"I can't remember a thing," I said racking my brains.

"Well you two disappeared for about an hour and when you both came back, she had the back of her skirt stuck in her knickers," said Elvis smirking. "I had my eye on her, you bastard."

"Oh sorry mate, you should've said."

"No worries," said Elvis with this wide pervy grin, "I had the knickers off that tall blonde piece in the fishnets. These posh birds don't mind putting it about do they?"

"So who's under the covers in the bed in the room?" I asked him.

Elvis started laughing, "You mean you don't remember?"

"I'm slowly coming round," I said, "but I can't remember a blonde bird."

"It's Blondie!! You idiot," Elvis shouted at me.

"Blondie? I can't remember a thing." For moment I tried racking my brains and I looked at Elvis, "I don't think I bonked her. Did I?"

"Are you kidding me?" Elvis's voice went up two notches. "You were banging her for hours. You woke me up twice, both of you were bouncing off the headboard and she was screaming her head off. She sounded like you were giving her a right seeing to."

"I honestly can't remember," I said staring back wide eyed.

"By the way," asked Elvis, "I bet you don't remember how you got that black eye do you?"

I shook my head, "I have no bloody idea."

"Well I do," said Elvis sniggering. "Blondie was making so much bloody noise screaming last night as you two were banging away, that I thought you were strangling her or something. I came in and you fell out the bed and smacked your eye on the side board."

"Bloody hell," I said, "I can't remember a thing."

"It was me who threw you back onto the bed," said Elvis
"You were spark out on the floor."
"Well do us a favor will ya, Joe?" I pleaded with him, "and
keep schtum. I can't be doing with Blondie on my case.
She's too bleedin' needy for me."
"My lips are sealed mate," said Elvis half laughing.
"I owe ya one mate." I went to leave the bathroom.
"Just a minute," said Evis "Don't you think you should
cover up?" I was so hung over I forgot I was still starkers.
"Ya don't want Blondie jumping on you when you go back
do you?"
When I came back in the bedroom Cary Grant was up and,
like the rest, looking the worst for wear and getting
dressed. Debbie Harry was sat up smoking and came
straight to the point.
"Did we end up in bed last night?" she asked me
sheepishly.
I sort of grimaced and she looked at me awkwardly and
said slowly. "Did we...er, do anything?"
It looked like she couldn't remember either and I looked at
her with a sly face and empathically shook my head.
"Nah!"
She winced all confused, looking suspiciously at me. "That
was one hell of a dirty dream I had then. I could have
sworn..."
"Well it wasn't me love,'" I lied back, "I dossed on the
bathroom floor with Elvis."
Blondie didn't push the issue. While Elvis claimed I had
bonked her, I just couldn't remember. Well, as far as I was
concerned, despite what Elvis had said, if she couldn't
remember and I couldn't remember, it didn't happen. I
mean I fancied her like hell but just for bonking, otherwise
she was indeed a bit too needy for me and I didn't want to

start something, especially with a work mate. I didn't want end up not being able to get rid of her, as she had a reputation for being a bit of a bunny boiler. Then there was the boss and she really did frown on the staff banging each other as it tended to cause friction when couples fell out.

When I was doing my Rod Stewart lookalike number, particularly if I was appearing at some posh do, the punters would expect me to be a good Rod Stewart as they were paying big coin for me to be there. I mean there were some lookalikes who looked nothing like the real celebrities. I mean, I've worked with a Sikh Elvis with full turban, a black Elvis, you name it. Saying that, they were really good guys and we had a helluva lot of good times. I suppose I look back now at age 62, and like most, you just wonder how time could move so fast from those rampant teenage years to being a 62-year-old grumpy fart. I sometimes look in the mirror if I dare, and I don't recognize the person looking back me. I like the reflection even less as each bloody year sails by with a greater speed than the one before.

I noticed as I got past a certain age, time seemed to speed up. All my mates say the same, the years just fly by and you start getting all these aches and pains and bits start going limp and few drop off. The young urges of youth get a bit less urgent and suddenly you are dropping your teeth in a glass by the bed. You are left wondering if you were ever young and whether it was all a dream. Sometimes you find yourself thinking about 'that girl' you had that magic moment with, and you wonder how things might have been different if you had stayed with her. But of course you are fooling yourself, because 'that girl' you are thinking about from all those years ago of your hedonistic youth, is still a young nubile girl in your memory and the truth is that time will have been just as cruel to her, as it has been to you. Yes, time takes the lot away from us and takes no prisoners.

But I was luckier than most. I had a good mother and father and good family. If my seafaring years travelling to all those foreign ports taught me anything it was there were millions, likely billions, who were living on the bones of their arses. So while I might moan a bit about life, I have had it better than most even though I would say we had it hard where we came from. It's all relative I suppose. I mean, today I still do occasionally get stopped in the street and people will point and say, "Hey, it's Rod Stewart." I took our lass to America a few years ago after a bit of a win on the horses, and we spent a couple of days in Las Vegas. I was continually stopped in the street and they would stop and say, "Hey, you look like Rod Stewart," in a brash American accent. I got drinks galore bought for me at the bar and they would take their picture with me. Recently in Hull, Rod Stewart was appearing at our local football stadium and the local Hull Daily Mail ran a story about my lookalike Rod Stewart days to coincide with his concert. For a few weeks I was like a local celebrity, even if I did get some catty remarks but I just ignored them. My fighting days are certainly over.

I have to admit that when I was young I always did my best to look like Rod Stewart as it had such an impact on the birds. It was like having a license to get their knickers off and when you're young you have a one track mind. Selfishly, looking back, I banged everything on offer. I hope you won't condemn me too much as we have all been young once.

CHAPTER NINE

So to give you a taster of more things to come, let's start with the story that started it all off. I'll jump back a few years to after leaving school. So here's how it all started. I was in the merchant navy, footloose, and fancy free. Rod Stewart had just come onto the scene and I really never gave it a thought, although I liked his song Maggie May. I would get the odd comment every now and again that I looked like him and I found that it became quite a good ploy for picking birds. Although most of the time they would pick me up and it was always the Rod Stewart thing they were interested in. I have to admit, I would usually end up getting their knickers off. Why wouldn't I since it was more often than not offered on a plate?

By now, Rod Stewart was getting bigger and bigger in the music scene, and as he did so more people would start saying I looked like him and sometimes I would get stopped in the street. I once did do a lookalike competition with the Top of Pops DJ Mike Reid as one of the judges, and he said to me he could not believe how much I looked like him. At that time, more than anything, I was just using it to pull the birds and get my end away. I was hot-blooded teenager so that will come as no surprise there then. I suppose I have to be honest, I'll admit I was banging the females ten to the dozen. God, was I one hell of a big headed arrogant young bastard or what? But we've all been young haven't we? And now I just look back and smile to myself. I have some regrets, but don't we all and I likely have less than most. I wasn't a bad person or anything, I just liked the ladies, and they liked me, so as they say in Hull: "I dipped my bread in" and loved every minute of it. Maybe that's why time went so fast, I was just enjoying myself. When I was at sea I worked hard, and when ashore I played hard and I milked the Rod Stewart angle for all it was worth.

So anyway, back to the story of how this Rod Stewart lookalike lark all started. It was the Queen's Silver Jubilee year and the ship I was on was in dry dock in Erith in Kent for a week or so. As most of the crew were from "darn saff" they were allowed to go home and I was asked if I would stay on board. I agreed (for a price, of course). It left only me as the bosun, the first mate, and one other young wet-behind-ears deck hand called Tony who was from Grimsby. I had some doubts about the first mate. You do bump into some real weirdoes at sea and he was a real classic weirdo. You tended to keep your back to the ship's bulkhead if you were passing him down a gangway, if you get what I mean.
Well one Saturday it was a lovely warm and sunny day, so me and this young Tony deckhand decided to go up to London for the day. Let's face it, the ship wasn't going to sink in dry dock was it? So off we toddled out of the dock yard gates.
There was a pub right next door so we decided to take refuge from the soaring heat and flies and have a couple of pints first, as you do, just to set us up. We had also liberated a small bottle of vodka from the ship's bond by way of keeping our boozing costs down and used it to

dram-up our pints and get pissed a bit quicker and cheaper.

Well, we had just sat down at the bar, which was strangely quiet for a usually busy back street bordello, when a harsh female voice called at us across the pub, "Hello sailor, buy a girl a drink."

Well I've come across all sorts of strange people on my travels at sea, and I mean strange people. Some I suspected came from a different planet. Anyway, I turned round expecting I know not what. If I thought this dulcet voice was going to be attached a hot bird, was I in for a shock. This bird was ugly, and I mean ugly. I think describing herself as a 'girl' was a bit of an exaggeration. She was fifty if she was a day. This cheap bottle-blonde in pancake make-up and bright red lipstick sauntered over to our table in these high heels she could hardly walk in, a tacky black velvet split skirt and these laddered black fish net tights with half a fag in the corner of her mouth. "Hello lads, I haven't seen you two in here before," she smiled with this fag bobbing about in the corner of her mouth.

Now I have to say it, and pubs next to docks are renowned for being frequented by Ladies of the Night, if you get my drift. I've never needed to use them and would never pay for a poke anyway because you never know what you will catch. So I always gave them a very wide berth. If this bird was looking for business, then she had shit out with me. This bird looked like she had been round the block more times than Chitty Chitty Bang Bang.

"Ooooh ya' know," she said with smile that revealed half her teeth were missing, "you don't half look like Rod Stewart. Get me a drink, and it might just be your lucky day. I'll do you for free, luv."

It was one offer I found very easy to turn down and I
diplomatically smiled, quickly finished my pint and
nodded to my ship mate to make a run for it. Next I knew,
Tony my young ship mate leans over with a wink. "If you
don't want to bang her, I'll have give it a bash. Ask her
how much?"
"Are you fucking kidding me?" I whispered back. "She
looks like she might be carrying the bubonic plague."
"Ya know your problem, Tez? Ya too picky."
And with that, he's at the bar and comes back with a drink
for her. Oh God, the young and foolish I thought, but he
was young with his brains in his pants and with a lot to
learn. I got the impression no matter what I said in
brotherly advice department, the throbbing in his pants
would get the better of him.
"How much luv?" he whispers into her ear. I roll my eyes.
I cannot believe he is going to bang this old boiler and
going to pay for the privilege. "Short time round the back,
a tenner," she makes her negotiating pitch.
"A fiver," my ship mate counters bluntly, "and that's my
final offer. Take it or leave it."
She puts down her drink and says to me, "Look after that
will ya luv?" and she goes to door with my mate eagerly
following and ten minutes later, they both return and my
mate has a big smile on his face.
"Do you want your freebie now, Rod?" she asks me. I can
see she is deadly serious.
Now sloppy seconds never appealed to me at the best of
times. I smiled: "Some other time."
"Suit yourself," she says and swigs down her drink. She
then lifts her skirt and gives me an eye-full. She is wearing
a black suspender belt attached to her stockings with a
pair of gusset-less black knickers for quick entry. "Think

of what your missing Rod," she pouts at me. My mate is by this time laughing his head off. "Go on!" he goads me, "Give it a bang."

It was not a pretty sight; I can tell you. The Black Hole of Calcutta sprang to mind. I tried not to wince and cracked a grateful smile at the offer. "I think I'll pass, thanks luv." She puts her skirt down, takes the goods off display and says to my mate in a whisper: "Is your mate a bit bent then? I know what some of you sailor boys are like. My young shipmate finds this highly amusing and rolls about laughing.

"No, I'm not bent," I snapped back, "I'm strictly a 'front door' man. Now just fuck off will you before you piss me off." I've always had a way with words as you can see. Anyway, I think this old boiler has got the message by now and she quickly disappears out the door with a final cheeky wave. "See ya Rod!"

I turned to my young ship mate. "Was it worth a fiver then?"

My ship mate sighed, "I just needed to empty my sack. Mind you, it didn't touch the sides."

We drank up and decided to look for more up-market surroundings so we wiped our feet on the way out and made our way up to the Smoke.

We wondered around Greenwich pub crawling and ended up in a pub right next to the Cutty Sark sea clipper. By now we were both well on our way to be being pissed and looking for some serious fanny.

Anyway, me and my mate go into this pub, get a couple of pints and sit down, just chewing the rug and having a natter, a laugh and minding our own business when this woman just walks over from nowhere and says to me: "Has anyone told you that you look like Rod Stewart?"

Now this woman was a bit older than me but still a sexy-looking boiler. The crocodile teeth were a bit off-putting but if push comes to shove, you can always put a bag over their head, and I was a bit drunk and they always look better when you've had a few. The ugliest bird can turn into Raquel Welsh when you've had a few drinks down your neck. Yes, not bad I thought, putting the teeth aside and given the chance, I wouldn't have passed up the chance to give her a good poking. In short, I thought my luck was in so I played it a bit canny. "Once or twice, why?" I said with a cheeky 'come on' smile.

"Because you're an ugly bastard, just like Rod Stewart," she suddenly lurched right at me. Any thoughts of getting into her knickers were definitely off the table now. She obviously wasn't a Rod Stewart fan. Just as you got compliments from the birds, you could get just as many insults on a bad day.

"And I thought we were going to be such close friends," I answered with a piss-taking voice. "Usually ugly old boilers of your age are looking for a bit of young cock but since you don't like Rod Stewart, I suppose a shag is out of the question?" My mate burst out laughing. "Now if I can't help you out with a shag. Fuck off will ya luv, I'm busy."

"Why you cheeky bastard!" she shouted back at the top of her voice, and before I saw it coming she had dumped her pint of beer all over my head. Actually, I've had so many pints thrown over me over the years I've lost count. I blame Rod Stewart for that. There are two types of birds who want to approach you - those who want to shag you and those who want to insult you. I don't know why they should want to insult me as I'm quite a nice guy. I put it down to that envious jealous streak in many people. Combined with a few pints, it brings the worst out in them.

Now I've been in this position loads of times and if I took the bait every time and lost my rag I would have been involved in too many fights and scuffles to count. So most of the time I would laugh it off and just take the piss and cut them down to size with my mouth.

While I can handle myself, I have a few seafaring mates who can also handle themselves much better than me. No matter how good you can handle yourself, it usually doesn't stop you ending up having a face like the Elephant Man after having far too many bar room brawls on foreign shores. I intended to keep my youthful beauty as long as I could.

Angrily, I stood up and wiped the beer out of my eyes.

"Look luv," I leered at her, "You better fuck off before I give your ugly face a makeover."

I mean I would never hit a woman but I considered making an exception for this pig-faced cow. Before the things could go any further the landlord was over in shot.

"You!!" he pointed at the woman "You're out and barred." Without hesitation, he manhandled her out the door and she tripped outside and fell into the gutter. The whole pub burst out laughing. She picked herself up and walked away screaming and shouting obscenities about Rod Stewart being an ugly bastard. I am sure they were aimed more at me than the real McCoy.

"I'm sorry about that," the landlord apologized, "she's always causing trouble somewhere, I'll get you a couple of pints on the house lads."

Who could argue with such an offer? So two free pints were duly plonked down at our table. "Cheers lads," said the barman.

It was hot as hell inside and so we took our beer and sat outside in the sunshine. It would help me dry off.

No more than a couple of minutes had passed and as we are drinking and taking in the afternoon sunshine another female walks over purposely in my direction and she's not bad looking either. This is going go two ways, I thought. It was either another swilling down with beer or I'll be toddling off back to her flat for a serious portion.

"If you don't mind me saying so..." this bird starts up.

I immediately cut in. "Look luv, if you're going to say I look like Rod Stewart forget it. I've just heard it off that other crazy bitch."

"Yes, I saw that," she said with a gentile smile and this amazing posh sexy voice. "I expect you get a lot of that?"

Well this is a better start I thought. My luck's changing and I must have smiled like a salivating wolf. She was very sexy and an older woman as well and I had a thing for sexy older women. In fact, I think I really just had a thing for birds any age, within limits and looks but before I could make my pitch she is pushing this calling card into my face. Oh God not a bloody escort tart now I thought.

"I work for a lookalike agency."

"Lookalike agency?" I took the card and read it. "A lookalike agency?" I said again with a puzzled face.

"Yes," she said excitedly. "I never seen a Rod Stewart lookalike as good as you."

"So what's your point?" I said, by now intrigued.

"Have you ever seen that woman who impersonates and looks like the Queen?" she asks.

"Oh yeah, I know who you mean," I answered.

"Well, we work with people like her and my boss runs the biggest celebrity lookalike agency in London. We do some of the biggest and best upmarket parties and occasions in the UK with lookalike celebrities."

By this time I knew getting this bird into bed was well off the table and this lookalike thing she was pitching just didn't interest me. I shook my head and pushed back her card. "I don't think I'm interested luv." I explained I was in the merchant navy and just in London on leave for a few days.

"Well, you should think about it," she said.

I shook my head again. "Don't think so luv."

Then she smiled with a sneaky expression on her face. "For a good Rod Stewart lookalike like you," she said slowly, "you would be looking at anything from £300 a day, up to £1,000 for a really upmarket society wedding."

"A DAY!!!" my mate burst out, almost choking on his beer.

A small note here. £300 to £1,000 a day and we are talking the 1970s here. Now that's real dosh.

Anyway, after getting over the shock, I gulped for breath and I snatched the calling card back. "Well, when I say I not interested, you might just have changed my mind."

"So what are you doing tonight?" she asks me.

"What do you have in mind?"

"My boss has a big wedding reception tonight in Knightsbridge and after I tell her what you look like I know she will snap you up."

"Won't I need to prepare or anything?" I was starting to understand this bird was deadly serious.

She smiled. "A little make-up here and there but you already look the part. Let me make a call and I'll be back." Two minutes later she's back. "You just got your first assignment. A taxi will pick you up here in half an hour. A room is booked for you at the Grosvenor House Hotel in Westminster."

"What about my mate? Can he come?"

"Yes, but he will have to stay in the room. The boss will meet you there."

"But how will I know her?"

She laughed. "Oh I'm sure she will find you."

Now this was all moving a bit too quick for me.

"But what if this agency woman changes her mind when she sees me?"

"Oh, I wouldn't worry on that score," she answers confidently. "I've worked with lookalikes for years and as lookalikes go, you're the best Rod Stewart I've seen and they are rare. In fact, I've never met any."

Before I knew what was happening this woman is pushing five crispy new ten pound notes into my hand.

"This is on account," she says, "The Grosvenor is expensive so don't go mad. The food and drink will be free at the reception but don't let the boss see you drunk or you'll be out, and just be discreet with the ladies."

"What do you mean?" I asked curiously.

"Although it's a society wedding these people do tend to let their hair down and go a bit wild, especially the ladies. So just be warned." She says the same thing again, emphasizing her words a bit more: "Just be discreet."

With that, suddenly a black cab pulls up and she ushers me and my mate into the cab and she gives the cabbie a tenner. "Keep the change," she tells the cabbie and we are off.

My mate is just loving it and says with a big smile: "Ya know what she means don't you?"

"What you on about?"

"About being discreet?" says my mate, "She means shagging a few of 'em. Don't get caught bonking."

"You've got a bleeding one track mind," I said shaking my head.

Now, although I'd been to London many times, it had always been hit and run visits, either passing through to Heathrow Airport on my way to catching a ship or being stuck on a ship on the depressing London docklands or maybe on some obscure out-of-the-way jetty. This was the first time I had been into the heart of the bright lights of London and the first thing that struck me was the traffic. The cab hardly moved as we started to get closer and closer into the central London. It was a strange feeling as we got closer as the scenery went from a tatty little pub in a dossy part Greenwich, to something out of a glossy upmarket magazine like Cosmopolitan. It was like being in a different world, a bit like a bright hustling bustling fairy land. To tell you the truth, I was beginning to get butterflies as we passed by ever more posher and palatial buildings. I was starting to wonder what I had let myself in for. This was not a world I felt very comfortable in. After all, my world was the northern hillbilly backwater called Hull. As is often said by strangers about Hull, the best thing about it is the road out. Mind you, don't knock it too much because it is my home town and I like it anyway.

Back in the cab, I'm still in awe of central London and staring out the window. Suddenly we are there and the black cab pulls up outside this hotel glistening in bright light and oozing money and wealth like I had never seen. Big chauffer driven limousines came and went like number 10 buses, and rich-looking people wearing top notch suits and dresses jump out and go inside the hotel. My heart was pounding just a little and I think my ship mate too had never seen the like of it. He just stared open mouthed. Then this big bloke dressed up all posh in this uniform and top hat opens the cab door. "What's he come as?" says mate my sarcastically.

"That's the concierge, daft lad," says the cab driver as this concierge bloke opens the door, and in a sharp Cockney accent I didn't expect, blurts out with sarcastic smile: "It's Rod Stewart!"

"He's with the lookalike party," the cabbie says to the concierge.

"Bloody 'ell," says the concierge in a brash Cockney laugh. "I've seen them all tonight. I've just seen Elvis, Alvin Stardust, Cary Grant and Aubrey Hepburn. Any luggage Mr. Stewart?"

"No," snaps the cabbie and with that the concierge escorts us in.

Suddenly I'm standing at the reception of this mega posh hotel and the place is full of people rushing around us, with woman and girls in ornate ball gowns and the blokes dressed like penguins in bow ties and black lounge suits. Already these posh birds are talking to me with plumbs in their mouths and grabbing my arm, screaming: "It's Rod Stewart!" Before I know it, birds are swinging on my arms at either side, cameras are flashing and I am totally over-awed and wondering what the hell I have let myself in for. Just an hour ago I was minding my own business just having a quite pint and now I was in the middle of this posh mayhem with ultra posh birds swarming around me just to get their picture taken with me. To say the least, I was scared to death.

"Take a picture of me with him," said one gorgeous bird, and she posed at me pouting her lips and waiting for a kiss, "Well come on then!" she snapped at me and she plonked a kiss on my lips and the cameras started flashing, and then another bird wanted a kiss and a picture and then another. My head was spinning. I was a total fish out of water. Thankfully, rescue is close at hand in the regal shape of the Queen. Not the real Queen I hasten to add, but the lookalike who leads me away with girls still hanging on my arm and takes me into this side room to meet the boss. Inside, I am totally struck dumb. I am being stared at by Elvis, Alvin Stardust, Debbie Harry, Nat King Cole. Marilyn Monroe and a smoking Polish Pope in all the white holy robes and a host of others. I can't take it in, it's all too quick and it seems like a dream.

"Well my assistant was right," says this very attractive posh woman. "She was right. You are a dead ringer for Rod Stewart." With that she gives me a room key. "The elevator is just down the hall. You're on the fifth floor for one night and you have to be out the room by 2pm tomorrow. Go and get settled for a couple of hours and my make-up girl will be up to touch you up." Was that an offer or what?

The boss looked at her watch. It was 5pm. "Be back here for 7pm. I'll give you a few house rules. Break them and you are out."

I got the feeling from her tone this lady did not piss ball about and I got her drift. She gave me a final parting shot: "And leave the mini bar in room alone until after the party. You'll have plenty to go at there anyway."

You might say I got a taster of what was to come as I squeezed into the lift going up with all these posh birds, and before I knew it, I was having my arse felt, someone was snogging me and another anonymous hand was squeezing and rubbing my crotch. I was being pulled in all directions, with hands rubbing and feeling me all over. Talk about dirty bitches, I was lucky to get out of that lift alive and it was only the quick thinking of the lift attendant that managed to pull me to safety on the fifth floor landing. He retreated back into the lift laughing, with all these wild half-drunk girls screaming what filthy stuff they were going to do to me at the party. I looked at myself in a nearby mirror and I had been totally abused. My zip was open, all my hair had been ruffled up and most of the buttons had been torn off my shirt. My ship mate standing next me, is just in fits of laughter. "You lucky bastard," he says with more than a hint of sour grapes "I'll have to stay in the room. Just make sure you bring a bird up for me after the party's over."

"Don't tell me, you need to empty your sack again."

"Just be a mate Tez," he says almost pleading, "There's loads to go round. These birds are top totty and just gagging for it. This must be a dream and I'll wake up soon."

"Are you kidding me? All you can think about is your dick. What about me!"

"What do you mean?"

"Did you see that lot in the lift? They were like a pack of hungry hyenas. I might not survive the night."

"Yeah, but what a way to go. Drowning in posh pussy."

My young ship mate was not so disappointed when we got in the room though. I think we were both in shock. The sheer luxury just slapped us right in the face. We stopped dead in our tracks and just stared in total awe. Now I am used to being bunked up waiting for ships in seedy back street seaman's missions or scruffy flea-bitten hotels with one dim lamp, a smelly mattress on a shaky bed and sheets last washed God knows when.

However, this hotel room was what I imagined Buckingham Palace was like. There were two single beds the size of two double beds, a big telly, an open mini bar, and on this massive antique-like sideboard was a big complimentary bottle of champagne in a big silver ice bucket. My mate did not need asking and popped the champagne cork and started swigging out the bottle. "Nobody is going to believe this when we get back to the ship."

"Do you mind? Save me some ya greedy bastard and remember this is my treat."

My mate laughed out loud and poured two glasses of Champers. "Whatever you say, Rod." We both looked at each other and started laughing.

My mate put the telly on and laid on top of his bed, drinking champagne and smoking away in his underpants as it was really hot in the room. I jumped in the shower and by the time I was out there is someone knocking at the door. I put on the free bath robe and went to the door. This gorgeous young blond piece pulling a trolley case stood waiting outside. "Hi I'm Tina, the make-up girl," she said in squeaky Cockney accent. A big waft of expensive perfume hits me in the face. "The boss sent me to touch you up."

How could I resist a request like that? I opened the door to let her in. She was staring with this big beautiful perfect white toothy smile that had me entranced. "Bloody 'ell, the boss was right," she said swooning, "You're the spitters of Rod Stewart." She sort of glides into the room, like walking on air, wearing these black high heels and black tight-fighting jeans. Her bum is just amazing, and for a second I can't take my eyes of her tight pert little ass as it wiggles by me. I won't elaborate what thoroughly dirty thoughts were going through my mind at that point, but I mentally promised myself that if I got the chance I would get myself a piece of that ass later. My uncouth ship mate is still laid on the bed in his underpants and his eyes almost popped out of his head. I saw him swallow hard as he looks at this bird.

"Oh, I better introduce you," I say all embarrassed, "This is a mate Tony, who's on the same ship as me." I throw him a big bath towel, giving him the hint to at least cover the bulge showing in his underpants.

"Can you do anything about this?" I ask, showing her the buttons torn off my shirt. "Some crazy birds in the lift almost ripped my shirt off."

This bird just goes straight into her case and pulls out a needle and thread set and a purse of buttons and in a few minutes my shirt is as good as new. Both me and my mate can't take our eyes off her amazing ass and her other assets. This bird was top totty.

"Bloody hell, you come well prepared," I tell her.

"I've been doing this a few years," she said with a knowing smile as she holds out my shirt for me to slip into, "but I should warn you, it won't last long."

"What do you mean?"

"Nothing to worry about," she said with a smile, "Just girly stuff, ya know."

"No, I don't know!"

"Well, you do look like Rod Stewart," she said sort of obviously.

"Yeah?"

"Well," she said awkwardly, "once they've had a few downstairs the girls can get a bit out rowdy."

I was getting a bit worried by now, "What do you mean rowdy?"

"Well, you know," she sort of said with a cheeky knowing smile, "You'll be like a trophy."

"A trophy?" I asked curiously.

"Yeah, they'll all want to shag you," she said bluntly with a shrug of her shoulders, "you know, just to brag they've been there."

My mate is squawking with laughter laid on the bed. "This gets better and better."

"But don't worry about it," Tina continues, "you'll be with all the others. Mostly it's Elvis and Alvin Stardust that cop it, but they all get ragged to bits. Just be discreet."

"I've been hearing that a lot today," I said by now sounding worried.

I think Tina could see I was getting a little nervous by this time, "Stop worrying," she reassured me, "You can tell this is your first time, it's always the same. Now none of them think twice about it. You'll get use to it."

After that she just sat me down, blow-dried my hair and dabbed a bit of make-up on my face. I got dressed and Tina adjusted my clothes here and there and then stood back to give me a good looking over last inspection, "Bloody hell," she swooned, "If I didn't know, I'd say it was Rod Stewart. I quite fancy you myself," she added with a smile.

"Well, if you're not busy later on," my ship mate Tony interrupts, "I'll be all on my lonesome up here, if you've got nothing to do."

Tina just wink at my mate: "I might just see ya later then," she tells him and she is gone out the door.

"Ooooh, did you hear that Tez?" says my mate getting all hot and bothered, "I'm in there."

"You must be fucking kidding. You're my guest. If anybody's getting into her knickers, it's me."

"You heard what she said. There's plenty to go round. Just save one for me."

I looked at my watch and it's ten to seven and my guts are rolling with nerves, and then the telephone rings and it's the boss. "We're all ready and waiting for you downstairs. Get down now, we're going in."

I closed my eyes and took a big intake of breath. My little heart was pounding and my guts swirling. "Right," I said nervously, "I'm off." I gave one last look in the mirror, and left my mate with a parting shot, "You fucking behave yourself."

"Don't you forget to get a bird for me," he shouts back and I'm out the door. The lift door opened and pile of drunken posh birds were squeezed in the lift and started screaming as the door opened. I decided discretion was the better part of valour and bolted down the stairs. They were all waiting for me in the hotel reception, a line of lookalikes. Elvis, Alvin Stardust, Cary Grant, Clint Eastwood as Dirty Harry, a really good Marilyn Monroe and this amazing Debbie Harry lookalike with a squawky voice standing next to the Polish Pope. Where the Polish Pope fitted into this caper I had no idea. So the boss waltzes up to me and give one last looking over, "Tina's done a nice job, you can get to know the others later." She seemed impressed. With that, she leads us into the main reception room. To say I had never seen anything like it would have been an understatement. It was like a Cinderella ball, but no-one was waltzing because it pure disco, with all these super rich people, already half-cut, chucking themselves around the dance floor in all sorts of mad dances.

"So what do I do?" I shouted in the boss's ear over the noise.

"Just copy what the rest do. That's our table over there. We'll be mixed up with other guests, your name should be at your place as your lookalike."

Before I could answer three drunken Hooray Henry girl types are on me and dragging me off towards the dance floor like they owned me. "What do I do?" I shouted in panic at the boss as they are dragging me way.

"You'll be fine, play it by ear. Just enjoy yourself."

At least I'm not alone because Alvin Stardust and Elvis are also being dragged along with me and suddenly we are lost in a scrum of girls dancing around us in circle. Elvis and Alvin are well up for it and wriggling their bodies all over the place. The girls are screaming and grabbing them all over and I'm being thrown around from bird to bird with endless wet drunken snogs coming in from every direction. I'm being groped all over and so is Elvis and so is Alvin Stardust. I think Elvis could see by this time I was looking a bit a worried with birds pulling us in all directions. "Just go with the flow," he shouts at me.

For the next four hours I find myself being groped under tables, snogged in corners, pulled into other side rooms and just generally being abused but in the most pleasurable way. I mean I was not complaining. I had lost count of the number of pictures I had taken with pissed up birds, and some 'odd' blokes, if you get my meaning. At one point I managed to drag myself off to the toilets just for some respite. I just stood there swaying from too much booze, looking at myself in a long mirror and pissing on my shoes. My face was covered in lipstick, my shirt was torn again and my zip was broken. If I thought I had reached sanctuary, I was soon disappointed (well not too disappointed) as make-up girl Tina walked into the men's toilets and stood staring at me with this cheeky face. "I see you've been having a good time."

I got the impression from the way she said it she had something else on her mind. She just about threw herself at me while I still had my dick in my hand, and she gave me this this oozing wet open-mouthed kiss, walking me backwards into a cubicle. The next I knew she was riving off her jeans and knickers and then started pulling down on my jeans. They soon were around my ankles along with my underpants and she was bouncing me off the wall for the next ten minutes. "My mate's going to be disappointed," I said, heaving at her through the snogs. "Don't worry about him," she said smirking. "I gave one of the girls your room number. She's gone up looking for Rod Stewart but she's too pissed to know who she's shagging by now and I doubt if she cares, just as long as she gets some dick."

I was so pissed by this time; I have no idea how long I was in that toilet cubicle with Tina the make-up girl. With all the booze I just lost track of time. I vaguely remember dancing some of the night away with Tina and then it all gets even hazier.

I woke up the next morning with one walloping hangover, the first of many lookalike hangovers to come. For a second I had no idea where I was. I was in someone else's bed and and someone else's room. I slowly pulled the covers from my head and Tina's head came out the covers too. She smiled and pushed her naked lean body on top of me and gave me a long kiss while pressing herself all over me. By now my engines were on full steam ahead. I looked at my watch. It was 11am. "I need to go, my mate will be wondering where I am," I said pathetically and weakening fast

She crawled on top of me and kissed me again, "Just twenty minutes," she whispered back at me urgently. It was such a deep hot wet kiss, that it went straight to my boots. "Ok, just twenty minutes," and it was back to business.

By the time me and Tina finally managed to get out of bed and dressed it was about an hour later. I hurriedly pulled on my jeans and slung on my shirt. Tina just slipped her jeans on and jumped back on the bed with no top or bra on, with the most magnificent pair of firm tits just staring at me. She lit a fag like she didn't have a care in the world and laid there watching me dress.

"So what's the hurry? I thought we might have a day in London, and go back to mine?"

"Believe me, I would love to but it don't work like that in my job. I have to get back to my ship." I looked at my watch and it was 12 o'clock. "I'm due on watch at 14.00 hours. I've got two hours to get back to the ship, or I'll be strung up by the yard arm."

"Pity," said Tina with a suggestive smile, "it could have been interesting. I can't remember a bang like last night in years. We'll have to do it again."

Believe me, just looking at Tina on the bed with these tight curvy jeans on and these tits just glaring at me, it was tempting to just jump on top of her, bang the arse off her and screw the consequences, but once you get a bad name in the merchant navy you soon end up getting black listed, and it's almost impossible to get a ship after that. So after handing me her number and giving her one last, long wet passionate kiss, I left Tina laying on the bed feeling as frustrated as I did. I certainly could have easily given her another hour's seeing to, but alas time was not on my side and I was quickly out the door.

I took the lift up to my room and wondered if my mate had already bolted back to ship without me. If I was worried about my mate, I needn't have bothered. The room looked like a bomb had hit it, with bottles, glasses and girly clothing and knickers littering the floor. I don't know what had gone on, but it looked like my ship mate young Tony had had a little party of his own. Suddenly three heads came out of the covers. Two were bedraggled birds with my smiling mate emerging between them.

"What happened to you, mate?" he asked with a big smile on his face, like a cat that had been at the cream. "As you can see there was more than enough to go round. This is Stephanie and this is Sue."

"Nice to meet you," I said quickly and threw my mate's jeans at him. "Just get dressed we're off."

"Oh look!" cawed one of these posh birds, "It's Rod Stewart. Are you getting in?"

Any other time I would have been up for the offer but to coin a phrase, I had no lead left in my pencil.

"Some other time ladies. Unfortunately, my friend and I have to go." I started to throw their clothes onto the bed in the way of a gentle hint to fuck off.

"Oh come on, Tez," says my ship mate all forlorn, "Come back in an hour."

"It's almost twelve o'clock," I said at him, "and if we are not back on the ship the captain will have our guts for a neck tie." I threw the rest of his clothes at him. The two girls slide back under the covers and my mate reluctantly climbs out of the pit. I straighten myself up with a quick look in the mirror, "You be downstairs in ten minutes' mate, or I'm gone without you."

Downstairs, all the lookalike crew were having breakfast along with the boss and everybody was in 'civvies'. I was amazed at the transformation. They all looked so different. To my surprise, Elvis was this little fat bloke with a bald head. We became good friends later and got into some dodgy scrapes together.

"Are you having some breakfast?" said the boss.

"I'm late, I have to get back to my ship."

"Oh, that's a pity, I have quite a few jobs lined up and I may need you."

I wrote down my home number in Hull. "Just leave any messages for me there."

"What about Monday?" the boss asked. "I've got the Village People coming. We're opening a country pub."

"I'll let you know, it all depends if we are still in dry dock. The boss gave me another business card with her private number on it. Then, as good as her word, she settled up in cash and counted out £250 into my little greasy palm in crisp new notes. I had never had so much money in my life.

"They'll be another £300 if you can make Monday," she said in a deliberately tempting voice.

CHAPTER TEN

My mate never shut up in the taxi on the way back about what these two dirty birds had done to him.

"I tell you Tez," he said swooning, "Talk about dirty bitches. Them posh birds are the worst. They just burst in the room and were almost raping me. Pissed out their heads they were."

"I take you had a good time then," I said sarcastically.

"Are you kidding me?"my young ship mate replied. "They had this white stuff they started snorting."

Now in the merchant navy you get offered all sorts of stuff in foreign ports, from hard drugs, to cheap fags and of course there are prostitutes galore hanging around every port. Now call me old fashioned but I came from a very straight-laced family and I had seen enough of the old sea salts who had destroyed themselves with both drink and drugs. As a result, I always kept away from such stuff.

"I hope you didn't snort any?" I said firmly at him.

"No chance but they must have slipped something strange in my drink because I was banging them both for hours, and I've still got a hard-on now."

"Yeah, well, if were you I would keep my mouth shut about this when we get back to the ship. If the captain finds out I've done a moonlight job he won't be best pleased. Drop me in it and I'll do you."

"My lips are sealed, mate," said Tony and he made the sign of a zip across his mouth.

As luck would have it, by the time we got back to the ship, it was still moored up and the captain told me repairs would take a few weeks. If I wanted, I could take some unpaid leave. It was up to me.

Any other time, I would have said no and just stayed aboard. That way, while it might have been a boring few weeks, at least I would have got paid for virtually just doing sweet FA. But the lookalike agency boss had a job lined up so I made my way back home to Hull for a couple of days and awaited her call. As good as her word, the call came, not on the Monday but on the Tuesday night. To my surprise, it was not the boss ringing me but this other woman. She said my name and number had been passed on by an associate she did not wish to name. I was intrigued. She said the job had been booked for a Thursday and she asked me if I could make it. She said they would be other lookalikes there but not the people I had met in London.

"No problem, if you're paying three hundred?" I probed diplomatically. I didn't want to sound too mercenary.

"This job's a bit different," she started awkwardly.

"What do you mean?"

"It's an opening for a gentleman's club.'" Again she lingered awkwardly. "It will be a sort of masquerade ball, and you will have to dress up."

"But I will be dressed up," I answered, "Like Rod Stewart."

"Well, er yes," she struggled on, like she was hiding something. She repeated "A gentlemen's' club" like she was expecting some penny to drop with me.

"I get the picture," I lied and an awkward cough came back down the phone.

"There are likely to be some ladie' there," she said slowly. "When I say ladies," she went on carefully, "I don't mean wives and girlfriends."

"What do you mean then?" I asked.

"Well," she continued awkwardly, "there will be wives there, but they'll be in another room." She coughed again. "I think it best, if you just play it by ear."

The penny then dropped with me big time. "Right," I said. I guessed it was some dodgy sex party scene. The type of dirty stuff you read about in those porno magazines like Penthouse and Hustler.

"I mean,' she quickly went on, "I'll understand, if you have objections but there will obviously be another fifty pounds in it for you.

"What three hundred and fifty? I'll have some of that."

"Just so long as you understand," she said down the phone cautiously. "Matters are kept very discreet."

"For three hundred and fifty quid luv," I answered stoutly, "I can keep a secret."

I have to say I was intrigued by the tone of secrecy in this women's voice, but if they were willing to pay me three hundred and fifty smackers, who was I to argue? So Thursday duly came and a taxi picked me up at my house around 1 pm. I thought that was a little early to tell you the truth. Now I thought this taxi was just talking me to the train station but it was no ordinary taxi. It was a private car and the driver told me: "I will be taking you all the way."

That's alright, I thought, and asked: "Where are we going?"

"Now this is going to sound strange," he said, "but I've been told I can't tell you."

"What do you mean?" You can't tell me?"

"Look," said the driver, "I just pick people up, and do as I am told."

I was getting a bit nervous now, and this was sounding dodgier by the minute. I mean, for all I knew this might be a bunch human sacrifice nutters and I had these visions of dark rooms, me laid on a sacrificial altar, big sharp knives and bits of me ending sprinkled around Stonehenge by dancing druids in the early dark hours. Funny how your imagination runs away with you.

"Now just a minute, this all sounds very dodgy." I think the driver detected the note of concern in my voice.

"Oh no, It's not dodgy like that."

"Then like what?" I asked him.

"Ya know," he tried to be obvious, raising his eyebrow, "it's one of 'those' parties."

"What parties?" I asked raising my own eyebrows.

The taxi driver rolled his eyes like I was being naïve. "I've been doing this run for a couple of years now and from what they tell me when they come out, I can definitely say, you will have a very good time." He gave me a knowing wink.

"It's not some sort of weird wife-swapping party is it?"

A big grin spread across the driver's face. "I'm saying no more than 'You're close.' Now do we go or not because I've got others to pick up on the way?"

I had a rough idea then this was some sort of rich peoples' orgy-type party. I wondered what I was getting myself into. This lookalike business was getting weirder by minute. I think this woman who had rang me had got the wrong idea about me. She must have had a low opinion of me if she thought I would be up for some perverted rich man's weirdo party where women could use me as a total sex object to do whatever perverted sex on me, and use me as a play thing, to ply me with booze and take advantage of me with their bodies. This was beginning to sound more like a Roman orgy than a lookalike party. The driver was still looking at me as I thought this thing over.

"Well?" he said at me.

"Drive on cabbie." I said with a big smile. "But if I end up under somebody's patio, I'll blame you."

The driver laughed and we pulled away.

We made three stops as we headed south of London. And what do you know, we picked up mate Joe, the Elvis lookalike in full uniform. It would be the start of a beautiful relationship and we would become big mates. We also picked up Clint Eastwood and Alvin Stardust. Joe gave me the full low-down on the party. "I've done a few of these. These people have more money than sense. If you ask me, they just like shagging with a bit of spice added. If our lass found out, she'd kill me, and I'd be out the door like a shot." Elvis winked at me with a cheeky laugh. "But the money's good and what the eye doesn't see, the heart doesn't grieve over, if you get my drift, Tez. If they want to pay me for shagging gorgeous women, who am I to argue?"

Now call me naïve if you like, but I'm just an ordinary young kid from Hull and, being a merchant seaman, I thought I seen and heard the lot. But this one was certainly a new one on me. I suppose you live and learn. Don't human beings get up to some weird stuff? While we peasants have to make do with Coronation Street, the rich and super rich have orgies. Oh well, who am I to judge? An old Hull saying came to mind, "JUST FILL YA BOOTS TERRY. LAY BACK AND THINK OF ENGLAND."

Now I can feel as something as a novice writer, I am going to have some problem describing the events that happened that night but anyway here goes. Just hold onto to your hat.

It was late and dark by the time we arrived at this big country estate. I could the see the approaching black silhouette of this big house about a mile down this private lane. We pulled up with a rustle on this big pebble-filled forecourt and the windows were flashing with coloured lights like there was a disco going on inside except the music didn't sound very disco but a bit sinister.

The cab driver looked at us all. "Well we're here," he said with a big smile, and we started to get out. He pulled away and we were left standing in this forecourt that was filled with every manner of expensive car, just lined up in rows. Elvis was looking at my worried face. "Stop worrying Tez mate," he said slapping me on the back. "You'll be fine." A big dirty grin spread across his face, "Get ready to enter Pleasure Island mate." He started sniggering.

I didn't know what to expect and was a little bit nervous. Anyway, we all approached this great big solid oak front door with these big stone pillars either side. Before we even knocked the door opened and two young giggling beautiful girls wearing multi colored eye masks beckoned us in. Inside it was like a mad house with people dressed up in every manner of scantily clad fancy dress, with men chasing women about all over the place. Everyone was wearing masks.

Suddenly all of us were surrounded by this gaggle of girls dressed like Raquel Welch in that famous movie One Million Years BC. They were wearing skimpy animal skin bikinis that hardly covered anything and masks. These girls led us down this great hallway with these crazies running everywhere. Every room we passed couples were just openly banging away. They were on chairs, spread-eagled on floors, they were doggying over couches and one couple were even on the top of a big grand piano. You name the position and they were doing it. I was totally dumb struck and had never seen anything like in my life. I could see my lookalike mates getting quite excited. I mean, why wouldn't you? I had to admit, if this was how the other half lived, then bring it on. These girls led us into this dark room and slammed the door. For a moment I couldn't see a bloody thing and then this low red very dim light started to come on and I couldn't believe what I was seeing. The place was decked out like one of those Arab harems with the women all decked out in velvet silky underwear and see through veils. The floor was covered with these large ornate cushions with all these women laid invitingly on the floor and beckoning us forward. As we walked closer the women seemed to rise up without effort and moved towards us. I remember a smell like incense filling the room and suddenly one of these women has my hand. I can see her smile through her veil as she leads me to quiet corner and slowly she lays me down. I could feel her start slowly to undress me and with hands exploring everywhere. I could sense the lights beginning to dim and this women lips were suddenly on mine. Within seconds the room was in total blackness and I could feel this women climbing on top of me. All the time, this odd drum music is playing in the background. I couldn't see a thing and by now I couldn't have cared less. Through all the moans and groans of ecstasy filling room, I distinctly hear Elvis saying: "Ahhh go on, go for it baby, go for it."

It seemed a good time was being had by all. The bird I was with was groaning: "Rod, Rod, go on, stick it to me Rod." Yes, she was definitely a Rod Stewart fan you might say, and who was I to deny her request, so I did as instructed. If I thought this was weird, after ten minutes it seems a game of musical chairs is taking place, and my partner has gone and another bird is on top of me. Now this bird feels a bit fatter than the last, much fatter in fact. I could hardly breathe as this fat bitch lay on top of me. I was thankful when once again we all changed place again, and I had what felt like another nubile body on top of me. Again time passes and my bird disappears into the darkness, and after a few minutes it looks like I've got no partner. So I scramble about in the dark feeling out for a female body. And bingo, my hand touches this body and I dive on it. Suddenly this voice says, "Is that you Tez?," It's Elvis. "Give it a rest will ya mate and take your hand off my arse!" "Sorry mate, I thought you were a bird." "Well I'm not, so piss of will ya mate, I'm busy here." I crawled off again feeling my way into the dark and soon found another willing vacancy and got stuck in.

We must have been in this room playing musical sex chairs for about three hours when the door is suddenly thrown open and light floods in. We are all laid naked across the floor in various stages of undress and compromising positions.

"Time's up ladies!" shouts this laughing bloke dressed up like one of those Arab harem guards, wearing a pantomime turban and mask. "It's time to join the party." With that the birds all get up adjust what little they are wearing and they scamper out the room giggling like daft girls.

This bloke then shouts: "Come on you lot. I hope you haven't shot your bolts yet, especially you two, Rod and Elvis, there are a few more ladies looking for a good seeing to."

"Is this for real?" I said to Elvis who was laid next me. He had this big dirty grin all over his face. "Yeah, good innit?"

"I can't believe they are paying us to bang their wives and girlfriends!"

"Take all sorts to make world, mate," said Elvis, "You've got a lot to learn mate. This is normal in their world."

"And I thought this agency was above board."

"Oh , the agency is. Don't ever this mention this to the , oss. She'll hit the roof."

"Who organized it then?" I asked.

"Tina, the makeup girl," said Elvis, "She's a dark horse I can tell ya. Just keep your mouth shut. Tina does loads on the side. Mostly weird parties like this."

"And I thought she was such nice a girl." I said all innocent. "I was getting quite stuck on her."

Elvis just looked at me. "I bet you've banged her, haven't you?" I sort of shrugged my shoulders for answer.

Elvis smirked. "Sorry to tell you mate but we've all banged Tina, she a nympho. Beautiful bird but can't keep her legs shut when there's a cock about."

My expression sunk. "And I thought I was special."

"Sorry to disappoint you mate. Anyway on your feet, "More work to do," he says with a big smile.

This party, if you can call it a party, it was an orgy really, and it was the damned weirdest thing I have done in my life. Sorry to say that's how this episode will end but I will say this, I never again did an appearance like that one.

There are indeed some weird people in the world. As a merchant seaman I thought I had seen it all, but what I saw later that night took the biscuit. Along with others, I left the gentlemen's club not long after leaving the harem. Now I am not a prude or anything. As I said, being a merchant seaman, you've usually seen the lot and in some third world countries I've sailed into I've seen some eye openers I can tell you. But later that night, this stuff was out of a Marquis de Sade novel. Now I don't mind a bit of kinky sex, but I do have my limits. Mine came at this party when the four of us were led into this room. I say room, it had the appearance of a medieval torture chamber to me. Anyway, inside were these leather-clad and leather-masked nubiles who ordered us to take off our clothes

"Is this what I think it is?" I said at Elvis.

"Don't worry mate. It's just a bit of bondage, they won't hurt you or anything."

"So what are the whips for?" I said a little nervously.

"It's their fantasy. They just want to tie up Rod Stewart," said Elvis.

"Then what?" I asked.

"Stop worrying mate." Elvis reassured me, "You're more likely to die of pleasure than pain, mate."

"How the fuck do you work that one out?"

With further ado, I was on my bike in panic and heading for the door in one hell of a great hurry.

On my way out, it looked as if the costume theme had changed. I've never seen so many birds dressed in leather carrying whips in my life. Anyway, I've said enough on this sorry episode already. If this place had got raided, I could have end up in the Sunday newspapers and likely in jail.

To give you a clue of what this caper was, just visualize a Roman orgy and you will get the picture.

Now I have to admit that after this weird party episode, I did not feel very proud of myself. In fact, I don't really know how I got sucked in. I should have bolted as soon as the door to that country house opened. But I was weak and as soon as I saw these beautiful girly wood nymphs running about, I knew what was rising in my pants was going to be my guide.

It was about four o'clock in the morning when I bolted from the party' and as luck would have it, the driver who had brought us was asleep in his car so I knocked on his window and explained the situation.

"Not your cup of tea eh?" he said with a little laugh. He explained that he was contracted to wait for the others but he could drop me off at the local station. I quickly took up his offer as I had a nasty feeling that if I didn't get going now, I might never be seen again. I suppose my imagination was running away with me but I had never seen anything like it in all my life, certainly not in Hull anyway. So after being dropped off at the local train station, for the next three hours I found myself freezing my balls off waiting to catch the early train into London before taking another train back to Hull from Kings Cross. Although I still did the lookalike assignments through various agencies, I never did one of Tina's parties ever again. I did, however, freely admit, to having many assignations in Tina's bed whenever I was passing through London. She was a hell of a looker, but Elvis was right. She was a total insatiable nymphomaniac and definitely not the type you could take home to Mum. Not a down-to-earth Hull Mum anyway.

CHAPTER ELEVEN

So anyway I'm still on leave at home in Hull because the ship is still in dry dock and the repairs are taking longer than expected. Although I was eager to get back to sea because I just loved my job, at least I had none of the usual money worries associated with not getting paid in such situations. Instead, I still had a big wedge burning in my arsehole back pocket from the lookalike jobs so I treated my Mum and Dad with a few expensive presents.

So expensive in fact, that Mum took me aside and with a stern face asked: "And just where are you getting all this money from?" She wasn't asking, as much as demanding. You've got to understand the world my parents came from. They were straight up, as honest as the day was long, and very old fashioned. They were Ten Commandment parents and expected the same from their children. I mean I had nothing to hide except the Roman orgy job and I wouldn't dare say anything about that but I tell them about being a Rod Stewart lookalike.

"THREE HUNDRED POUNDS!!" she shouted at me, "And who's this Rodney Stewpot? I'm not sure I like the sound of this Rod Stewpot person. And three hundred pounds...Pull the other one my lad," she scowled at me with a mother's accusing face.

At this time, I suppose I was about 22 years old and like all families there was a generation gap. My Mum had no idea of who Rod Stewart was and why should she? If Top of the Pops was on in our house, my Mum and Dad would just look at all us watching with total disapproval, "They look like a load of pansies to me," my Mum would say, shaking her head.

"Mum," I said, "Rod Stewart is one of biggest pop singers in the world."

"And they give you £300 because you look like him?" she snapped back, "I think you're pulling my leg, me lad." She had that look on her face only mothers have in such circumstances. "I'm going to talk to your father about this. If I find you are up to something you shouldn't be, don't think you are too big to get your backside tanned me lad." And that was my Mum.

After making her own enquiries, she did reluctantly accept my explanation though she found it hard to believe that anyone would pay me such a large amount of money just because, as Mum would say, "I looked like one of those pansies on Top of the Pops."

So one night, it's Thursday and Top of the Pops comes on the TV and up pops Rod Stewart singing. Mum suddenly pipes up in shock: "Bloomin' 'eck, is that him then, Rodney Stewpot?"

I shook my head and laughed. "That's him Mum."

She got up, looked closely at the TV screen and then looked disapprovingly at me and said: "You look nothing like him. He's an ugly bugger." With that, she went to put the kettle on.

I've got one week left before I am expected to report back to the ship, and the agency boss has a wedding party do for some rich bird down south. Apparently this bird is a big Rod Stewart fan and her rich brother has paid for me and some other lookalikes to be surprise wedding presents.

So I'm back on the ship midweek and bunking up onboard to save me hotel fees. I'm getting paid but we are not due to sail to Sweden for another few days. The agency boss sends a taxi straight to the ship to pick me up and I am whisked away. On the way down we pick up Elvis Presley, the Polish Pope, Clint Eastwood and there's a new kid on the block in the form of Albert Steptoe. The Steptoe and Son BBC sitcom was massive at the time, a hit across the world.

The taxi driver just couldn't stop laughing because he loved Steptoe and Son and this Albert Steptoe not only looks like Albert but could imitate his voice as well. This bloke was funny with it and had this taxi driver in stitches every time he said: "Harold, she blown you out!" It was one of Albert's famous sayings from the show, if you didn't know.

The boss has told us that there will also be a lookalike competition with the winner getting a cup, fifty quid and a bottle of champers. The lookalike who gets the loudest cheers wins.

The venue was in Bisley, about an hour's taxi ride from where my ship was moored. Although my mate Elvis was in the taxi with me, he never uttered one word about what had gone on a few nights before and it was clear he was keeping his mouth shut. Now even though I was young, I was a quick learner and I had the impression that behind some of those masks at the country party might have been a few famous faces. I'm also going to make a confession here. During that party I did have occasion to go to the toilet for a slash and just for a second there was a bloke in there with his mask off. As I entered he put it back on pretty sharpish and rushed out. Now I am not saying I could be certain, but the face I saw looked like a pretty famous sitcom actor to me. At least he was famous at that time in the 1970s. Several years later I read in a story in one of the Sunday newspapers about this very same actor being famous for similar orgy-style parties at his house.

The wedding was at a big posh country hotel and we were all duly dropped off and went inside. Other lookalikes were there waiting for us. I think Debbie Harry must have got her memory back from the last time we met and was over like a shot, putting her arm in mine like we were an item. I had the feeling she was staking an early claim on me and looking to replay our night of long drunken passion.

The boss came through from the banqueting hall and told us the party hadn't started yet.

"I've booked you all a room." She stared with a look of disapproval at Debbie Harry holding onto my arm and she gave me a room key first.

"You are on the second floor Terry," she said with a nice warm smile. Her expression changed as she handed Debbie Harry her key. "And you are on the fifth floor," she said, before aiming her next sharp words in Debbie's direction. "I expect you all to sleep in your own rooms. We don't want a repetition of whatever was going on in your room last time do we?"

"I'm sure I don't what you mean," Debbie Harry snapped back at the boss in her bimbo blonde Essex squeaky voice. The boss did not hold back and gave Debbie a verbal broadside: "I was in the next room and the bed banging on the walls kept me and many others awake most of the night." She paused, staring straight at Debbie. "Along with all the other beastly sounds coming through the walls."

"And you Terry," the boss said turning to me, "I've got a special job for you."

I was intrigued. "And what's that?"

"Rod Stewart is the bride's favorite singer and so you'll come out last and give her a big surprise. After that, read the telegrams, cards and messages. Just stay in your room until I call you. So don't make a hash of it and keep away from the alcohol in the room until afterwards please."

"Right boss," I replied obediently. For three hundred notes, I would have kissed her ass. Mind you I would have kissed her ass for nothing as she was a very tasty lady with a very tight figure. Unfortunately, she was also totally straight laced and didn't shag the employees. It was a shame because I would have certainly slipped her a crippler no mistake. I think she knew she was oozy and sexy and, I guessed, a bit of cock teaser. I got the impression she liked playing hard to get and that was what made getting into her knickers even more exciting. But she was off-limits, forbidden fruit. I don't know if it was wishful thinking but I always seemed to get a special sort of smile off the boss. A couple of times I had been tempted to try it on with her but I didn't want to blot my copybook with her, as the big money I got paid for these lookalike jobs was just too much to lose and it was money for old rope. As a deck hand at sea, I got paid about £30 quid a week. In contrast, just a few hours pretending to be Rod Stewart, and I could clear £300 and sometimes £500 a spot, with all the free booze, free food and shag on tap thrown in. What's not to like? I imagined the real Rod Stewart would have been proud of me, flying his colours with as many notches on the bed post as he did. Well, maybe not.

"I've booked you all in for two nights so you won't have a mad rush to vacate your rooms tomorrow, and you can let your hair down for a day," said the boss. "I'm sure it will give some of you time to recover. Now off you go and smarten yourselves up."

So we all bolted for the lift and our rooms.

Now if there was one thing about the boss, when it came to spending a bit of money on taking care of us she did not spare the horses. No, she was definitely not tight-fisted and the hotel room was out-of-this-world luxury. I had a big double bed, en suite bathroom and a massive mini-bar filled every exotic beer and spirit you could name. I stripped off my day clothes and wrapped a towel around myself in preparation for a shower. Defying the boss's instructions, I poured myself a quick vodka and tonic and promised myself just one little drink and that would be it. I sat on the bed relaxing and watching the Sale of The Century game show on TV with that toffee-nosed knob Nicholas Parsons compering. The show was my favourite for no other reason than I had the throbbing hots for the black-haired hostess Christine Owen, if I remember her name correctly. She was the one with the beefy long legs and big tits. She had made several nocturnal phantom visits to my lonely cabin while at sea when I was creaming one off while perving and fantasizing over the poster of her I had on my cabin wall, wearing only a bikini and showing off a box like a monkey's fist.

Anyway, while I'm laid there minding my own business watching the telly and Christine's luscious juicy legs, there's a knock at door. I roll my eyes and reluctantly answer it. Standing there is this gorgeous, black haired hotel maid, dressed like a little sexy French maid, wearing this very short black skirt and frilly apron with these shiny smooth legs in black nylon. I just cannot take my eyes off her legs - she had the most, thick firm riding thighs you have ever seen. This bird looked like she had just come out of a sexual fantasy and her big wide white smile was staring at me.

"Excuse me, sir," she said in this smoothed-out south of England accent, "Compliments of the house, and I just wondered if you would like a drink or anything."

Now don't get me wrong, I was grateful to be asked but something did not quite ring true with this little situation. I threw my door wide open and pointed at the fully stocked mini-bar. "I think all I need is just there luv, thank you very much."

"Oh well," she sort of said hesitating, "I thought I would just ask. Is your room OK?"

"Fine thanks." I smiled as the penny dropped.

"Well, if there's anything else, you can think of?" she said lingering, and then suddenly blurted out: "I just love Rod Stewart. I'm his biggest fan."

"Well I'm not the real Rod Stewart," I answered laughing.

"Yes, I know that, but hey," and she smirked right at me. "If there's anything else I can do for you?" From her suggestive tone it was obvious what she meant.

Well even I can take a hint and I didn't need asking twice. I opened the door and invited her in. "I suppose I could find you something to polish," I said with a grin which was quickly returned, and she stepped inside. I laid back on the bed and never took my eyes of her, as she slowly flitted around the room slowly polishing, bending here, and bending there. What with Christine Owen on Sale of Century showing off a prize boat in a swimsuit I was throbbing and bulging big time. By now she is polishing the bedside table and is so close that I can smell her sexy perfume and the swish off skirt is touching me. Next, her black nylon-clad leg brushes my bare leg, and surprise, surprise, she trips and falls on the bed with a giggle and is within kissing distance. She suddenly plants a big long wet, open mouth, tongue dipper right on my lips. I pull her full on the bed, my towel has fallen away, I pull up her skirt, and I half slide down her tights and knickers, only for her to pull them down more urgently. Without even aiming I slide straight in with no questions asked and she lunges her hips towards me. It was like sliding your knob into a tight warm roll of liquid velvet. I never bothered taking off the rest of her clothes, as shagging a fully clothed French maid was always one of my fantasies. If it hadn't been for the phone ringing an hour later, I would have been up her for ages. Slip Sliding Away, as the song goes. I picked up the phone trying to restrain my hot breathing. It was the boss giving me the heads up, "Be down in half an hour!"

"Right boss," I answered, "Half an hour." I put down the phone and looked at the maid under me. "We've got ten minutes." She launched another hot urgent kiss on me, and for the next ten minutes she rived me across the bed like crazy women in agony, until suddenly, we are both grunting and groaning and a few seconds later, I fell onto her with sweat pouring off me.

"God, that was good!" she said. "I needed that. A good shag takes away all the tensions of the day."

I laughed back and gave her a quick kiss.

"I couldn't agree more. Look, I need a quick shower and need to get dressed."

"Can I come back later, after I finish my shift?" she said looking up at me, with another one of those suggestive smiles.

"I don't know what time I'll be finished but take one of the key cards if you like," I shrugged.

"It's a date," she said with a suggestive smile and she squeezed my knob. "I want some more of that, Rod," she said slowly with a cheeky smile.

Don't worry on that score, I thought, there's a lot more where that came from, a hell of a lot hell more.

After a speedy dip in the shower, five minutes later and I'm dried and dressed with my hair blow-dried. I took one last minute to look at myself in this full length mirror, and couldn't help admiring myself. "You gorgeous bastard," I said aloud to myself. I then sprayed a couple of puffs of deodorant under the old pits with a quick blast down the front of my pink trousers as you never know after all who could end up swiveling from it later on.

The boss was waiting as I came out the lift and she gave me one last inspection. She smiled with this approving grin. "Yes, if I say so myself, you could be the real Rod Stewart."

The boss explained that the others were already inside the banqueting room and the speeches were just finishing. My job was to sneak in from the back and stand behind the bride, and the groom would ask her to close her eyes and turn round and I would be her big wedding day surprise. So off I went and stood behind the curtain until I heard the magic words. The groom's speech seemed to go on for ages. I got the impression he liked the sound of his own voice and was something of a comedian as howls of laughter were coming from the seated guests.

So then comes my bit and I hear the groom start up: "This has been one of the happiest days of my life to marry this beautiful girl standing next me." A round applause rises up and some cheers and some table thumping and then,

"Well I have a bit of a surprise for Miranda." I took it Miranda was bride. "Well Miranda, I want you to close your eyes," the groom announced all excited.

Now that's my cue so I push through curtains and the screams start. These screams from the ladies in the room were so loud they shocked me. They think I'm the real Rod Stewart. Now this bride might be in for a shock when she opens her eyes, but I got a big shock too. This bride is over thirty stone and the size of a house. She was so ugly she made Miss Piggy look like Kim Basinger. And to top it all, she had a patch over one eye. The groom was this little skinny guy that a wet fart would have blown over. I could just see this fat bride sitting on his face during a moment of passion on their honeymoon. She would kill him. No exaggeration, she was fucking massive and ugly wasn't a good description. I mean she must have so many rolls of fat oozing from her body, the honeymoon would be a magical mystery tour, ending in, 'Fart and give us clue where it is?'

Suddenly hubby shouts: "Open your eye Miranda!" and this one-eyed fat bird is staring straight at me. She suddenly starts screaming in hysterics, then begins to run towards me. It's like a juggernaut coming towards me at me full pelt and suddenly she has me in this excited bear hug and lifts me off the ground. So she plonks this enormous soggy full on open mouth kiss right on me and is sucking on me like an industrial vacuum cleaner. It was like someone has stuck a sink plunger on my face. For a minute I couldn't breath and I thought I was going to pass out, what with her face stuck to mine and gripped in this sumo wrestler bear hug. The crowd was up and cheering and I could see all my lookalike mates just lapping up my agony.

Then suddenly this fat bird just drops me like a sack of spuds and I fall onto the floor. The crowd thinks it's so amusing. Then this fat bird bride turns to hubby all starry one-eyed and luvvy dovey and squawks back at him with tears in her one eye: "Oh Rupert, you knew I loved Rod Stewart. Thank you my darling." Next she is giving hubby the bear hug treatment and I'm thinking if only I could be a fly on the wall in their honeymoon bedroom. The film would be worth a fortune.

After surviving the bride's assault I'm beckoned forward and a pile of cards telegrams and messages are passed to me. For the next fifteen minutes I am at the head of the table with all of the eyes of the guests on me, and I'm reading all the good will messages, and getting the audience laughing as well with a bit of ad-lib. I can see I'm getting come-ons from a few birds looking on. So I finish reading the messages and the best man announces: "PARTY HAS STARTED, THE BAR AND BUFFETS ARE OPEN." It was trough time and I was so hungry I could have eaten a scabby horse. (That's Hull saying by the way) Then, just my luck, what blasts out of the speakers but Rod Stewart's 'Baby Jane' and this big fat bride steps forward for the the first dance and she pulls me onto the dance floor with all the subtlety of a caveman who has just found a mate. The guests have gathered in a circle and are dancing and clapping their hands like a tribe of Red Indians dancing around a totem pole. Now this fat bird bride is fucking massive with hips the size of a plough horse and she insists on bumping and grinding me all over the dance floor. Now I don't mind having a dance, but every time this fat bird bumped me I flew several feet across the dance floor much to the amusement of the guests. Thankfully the record ended and this bride gave me one last sink plunger kiss and was dragged away by new hubby to mingle and no doubt stuff her face with most of the wedding cake.

By now the bar is open and buffet is in full flow, the lights are lowered and the flashing disco is in full swing with everyone boogying on down.

Now I've done a few of these big rich wedding do's and they tend to have a life of their own. After a few hours, the drinks have well and truly loosened everyone's inhibitions and they turn into wife-swapping parties with everybody dancing and kissing and groping with somebody else's wife or girlfriend. And somewhere you can guarantee, in some dark corner of the gardens or under tables, knickers are being dropped for a quick spicy jump, that you can blame on too much drink in the morning.

Now I was still exhausted from banging the chambermaid and I still hadn't spotted another bird at the party worth giving up for in exchange for getting the maid back in bed. By this time, Debbie Harry is doing her usual drunken routine on the stage and giving it loads on the karaoke, showing off her knickers and her mile-wide thigh gap just for good measure. I mean just looking at her up there on stage and her magnificent wide box, and it would send a yearning urge to the pit of your stomach.

Unfortunately, while she might be beautiful and sexy, as I said earlier, she was far too needy for me. Although the thought of slipping between her legs made my pouch bulge, after the last time I knew I would have one hell of a job of getting rid of her. While all I wanted was a bang, she was the type of bird that would be planning the wedding afterwards. I think deep down all she wanted was to get some sucker's ring on her finger, a little house, two kids and an easy life while some mug paid for it all. Well

thanks, but no thanks, that mug would not be me. I was
still young and wanted to sow some more wild oats.

I was not so drunk that night that I didn't know what I
doing, and despite having a gaggle of birds dragging on my
arm, the earlier antics with the chamber maid had
dampened any urgings in my loins. In fact, I was quite
tired and just looking for quiet corner to silently get drunk
in, and maybe sneak off to my room but with all these
birds wanting photos and dances, there wouldn't be much
chance of that. Now you might find this hard to believe,
but you can very easily get fed up of a good thing. I had
been doing this Rod Stewart lookalike thing for a few
years now, and you can get fed up of the attention, and
believe it or not, you can very easily get fed up of gorgeous
birds especially. I had banged so many birds at lookalike
parties and in foreign port when at sea, I had literally lost
count. At one time I did count, but after a hundred I didn't
see much point. Being a Rod Stewart lookalike, the birds
were just there. After a while I suppose I just took them
for granted. It was just bang and Terry was gone. In many
ways I suppose, I became a bit blase about the whole thing.
I mean, they didn't really want to screw me did they?
They wanted to screw Rod Stewart. I was just cashing in
on their self-delusions. After a while I suppose I got a bit
callous with girls. I put it down to getting too much of a
good thing. At the height of my Rod Stewart lookalike
career, me and my mate Elvis ended up in this hotel room
after a party with five very fit birds, just drinking and
banging the night away. It was a bit surreal really at the
time but I was living in a surreal world at that time.

So anyway, I have managed to quietly to slip away into this
dark corner at this party and am stood leaning on a wall

pouring God knows what down my throat from this bottle and just drinking myself into oblivion and I suddenly get the Polish Pope lookalike tugging on my arm. He is pissed up to the eyeballs, and has this old boiler - a Cruella De Vil lookalike in her own right - hanging on his arm. He is also smoking and waving his fag around and nearly pokes me in the eye twice. "Hey up, Terry," says the Pope, half spitting all over me. "Ya know Terry, I consider you one of my best mates."

Isn't strange when people get pissed they always get emotional and want to pledge eternal friendship.

"I like you too Pope baby," I tell him back over the noise.

"Ya know Terry, that lot think you're a big head."

Yes, it's funny how a bit of drink starts to loosen lips.

"But not me Terry, mate," the Pope drunkenly assures me. "I consider you the salt of earth."

The Pope was totally out of his head by now and talking absolute shit, as drunk people tend to do.

"Well thanks for that Pope," I answered trying to move away and made my apologies. "I think I need a drink. We'll talk later."

The Pope jokingly made a sign of the cross, "Bless you my son, and go in peace." Then he leans over and whispers in my ear: "I'm just popping in the garden, and I'm going to bang the arse off her."

I looked at the drunken old boiler hanging onto his arm who looked totally out of game and smiled.

"Give her one for me, Pope baby," I whispered back.

"Don't worry," he said with a dirty laugh, "I will." They both staggered off heading for some dark place in the garden for a knee trembler.

The strange thing about being totally wasted is that time just whizzes by. I suspect that sometimes you get so pissed that you black out and don't remember a damn thing. I've done that a few times.

Now something strange happened to me at this wedding do, as I remember. I was leaning on the wall in a quiet corner of this party slinging the contents of this bottle down my throat and slowly but surely I am sliding down this wall I am leaning on, ending up flat out on the floor. I can still hear the music blasting around me, and people coming and going and stepping over me. Yes, I am totally pissed out my eyeballs and out cold but I can still feel myself being dragged along the floor with the faces of two giggling girls flashing above me. What happens next is a bit hazy. I'm in a totally dark room and someone is sucking on me like a pair bellows while some other bird is kissing me. I am too pissed to care but one thing is for sure and that is the girl sucking on me is getting the desired results, and now someone is astride of me having their wicked way. At this stage I am so drunk, I am not sure if I am dreaming or if this is for real, but either way, I'm not complaining. Then I get the sensation that someone has climbed off me and another is astride of me and riding me with a vengeance.

I have often thought back to that night, and to tell you the truth I was so pissed I can't remember if it was a dream or whether it really actually happened. All I remember for sure was coming round with the groggy face of another lookalike mate floating in front of me. It was Alvin Stardust, slapping my face and patting me with ice water to bring me round. "You alright mate," he is saying at me. "What happened?" I said.

"I don't know," answered Alvin Stardust, "I just found you flat on your back on the floor with your pants round your ankles. Two lasses just bolted out as I came in. I think you've been molested mate. Do you want me to call the police?" he said laughing, helping me to my feet.

"You need to shape up mate," said Alvin. "It's the lookalike competition and the boss wants us all on stage."

I don't know how long I had been out for, but the clock on the wall in the banquet hall pointed to midnight. I spent a few minutes puking my guts up in the toilets, and after straightening my hair and clothes in the toilet mirror, I was as good as new. Then, on closer inspection, I noticed my neck covered in love bites and when I went for a piss, my knob was covered in thick lipstick. I think Alvin had been right, I had been molested, but I was dammed if I could remember a thing about it. While I am still pissed, I am not so pissed I can't pretend to be sober so I pull myself together for the competition and try and walk straight as I come out the bog. Who do I walk straight into but the boss and I can see she is angry. "And where the hell have you been?" she shouts at me. "Everybody has been looking for you. The competition was supposed to start an hour a go."

Now although I could put on a straight walk, I was still too drunk to talk properly, and my mouth went all rubber and drunken gibberish came out. "Soooryy I woont dooo ittt agaaaain bosssss."

"You're drunk!" she shouted at me. "Well you just buck yourself up and get on that stage and don't make a fool of yourself or you'll regret it."

She just about frog-marched me to the stage to stand with all the rest but I don't know why she was having a go at me. From what I saw the whole crew were pissed to the eyeballs.

So the line of us lookalikes are led up on to the stage and we all are stood on there when this big spotlight goes on and big cheer goes up from the guests. The DJ then comes to compere the competition.

"Well ladies and gentlemen, here they all are. You name the celebrity and we have them. Not of course the real thing, but the poor man's version!" All the guests laugh. What a prat, I thought. The poor man's versions, eh?

'Well, it's up to you ladies and gentlemen," continued the host, "the spotlight will travel down the line of our lookalikes, and the one with the loudest cheer wins the completion. ARE YOU READY?!"

A big cheer goes up. The spotlight starts on Dirty Harry and a big cheer goes up. Then it's Cary Grant and another cheer. Harold Steptoe gets a louder cheer and so it goes on down the line. There are about ten of us, I can't remember the exact number, and then the spotlight is suddenly on Debbie Harry and her skirt is right up her arse with her wide box on full show. A massive cheer with wolf whistles galore fills the room, putting all the previous cheers in the shade. It looked like Debbie would win. Then the spotlight was on me and I got a good cheer too but not as loud as Debbie Harry, for obvious reasons I might add. Last of all the spotlight went on the Pope and his Holiness mockingly gives the crowd the sign of the cross and slings the drink he is holding down his neck. The crowd are in stitches and this huge cheer went up. It was difficult to judge if the cheer was louder than for Debbie Harry and then cheekily the Pope steps forward and says into the microphone: "Bless you my children." The crowd are just loving it and another great laugh goes across the room.

"Well," announced the DJ, "I think we have a draw. Can I ask His Holiness the Pope to step forward and the gorgeous Debbie Harry?

Debbie Harry walked forward arm in arm with the Pope, still showing off her box as she oozed forward temptingly, with all the men wolf whistling and cheering.

"Now," said the DJ, "I'm going to hold my hand over the head of each celebrity and the loudest cheer wins.

First came the Pope and a loud cheer, then Debbie Harry and another similar loud cheer. It was a close thing. I certainly couldn't tell who got the loudest cheer but since I was pissed to the eyeballs, I didn't know what planet I was on anyway.

"I declare a draw!" announced the DJ and the guests all cheered. "I now call on Miranda, the beautiful bride to step forward to award the prize."

The bride was so drunk she staggered onto the stage, ripped the microphone out the DJ's hands and pushed him aside like he wasn't there. Then she starts drunkenly ranting into the microphone. I don't think anyone could understand a word, I know I couldn't. Anyway, both Debbie and the Pope step forward and collect their £50 prize in white envelopes but they only have one trophy and when the bride presents it both, the Pope and Debbie Harry start a friendly tug-of-war over it. Suddenly the tugging gets less friendly, and Debbie Harry loses her grip as the cup is ripped from her grip in one big pull by the Pope who goes hurtling forward and falls off the stage. By now the boss is hanging her head in shame, no doubt hoping the ground would swallow her up. So endeth another sorry episode. We all marched off stage in all directions and I went outside for a fag.

I was stood there minding my own business and I can see this Rolls Royce swaying from side to side. I guessed what was going on inside and couldn't resist a peek. I crawled up to the car, peeked inside and there is Albert Steptoe

with the Pope's old bird, Cruella de Vil, in the back seat.
Albert still has his hat on and this old bird has her legs up
on the car ceiling, and all I can see is Albert Steptoe's little
shiny bum pumping up and own in the moonlight.
Suddenly he sees me looking in the window and he smiles
with this big dirty grin on his face just like the real Albert
Steptoe and sticks his two fingers up at me. I got the
message and left Albert poking his truncheon into what
must have felt like an old soggy grapefruit.
I went back inside and the music had started up again.
Elvis was giving the Pope some first aid to his head wound.
If only the Pope knew his bird was getting a good seeing to
outside. Anyway I went up to see how the Pope was.
"How are you mate?" I said all animated and false. Truth
be known, I was still too half cut to care but I showed the
flag.
"That fucking Debbie Harry, the bitch!" snapped the Pope
holding his head. "Did you see the cow push me? I'll sort
the bitch later." Then he changes the subject. "Hey, Terry
mate, that bird I was with earlier, you haven't seen her
have you, mate? She was supposed to wait for me after
the competition. I was hoping to get into her knickers."
I don't know why but I just couldn't resist it. "Oh yeah
mate, I just saw her outside. She said to tell you she'll be
waiting for you. She's in sat in the back of the blue Rolls
Royce outside."
The Pope's eyes lit up and he was suddenly on his feet.
"You need to take it easy Pope mate," said Elvis, "you had a
bad bang on the head."
But there was no stopping the Pope, "Yeah well, I've got
another type of bang on my mind." The next thing I know
the Pope is rushing off out the exit.

Elvis just shook his head. "You'd think at his age he'd have given up feeding the hedgehog."

I just couldn't help laughing.

"What you laughing at?" said Elvis suspiciously, "what you up to?"

"The Pope will get a shock when he catches up to that old rich boiler," I said smirking.

"What do you mean?" asked Elvis.

"She's in the back of a Roller outside with Albert Steptoe with her legs around his neck."

"Come on!" said Elvis laughing. So we both rushed off to see the fireworks.

We got outside just in time to see the Pope open the Roller's back door, no doubt hoping to fill his boots. So the Pope opens the door, and a fist comes flying out and smacks him right in the mush. The Pope rolls backwards onto the ground for a bit but then he's back on his feet and just dives in the back. By now this Rolls Royce is violently rocking from side to side with all sorts of noises, shouts of abuse and screams coming from inside. Suddenly Albert Steptoe and the Pope fall out the back scrapping like a couple of alley cats. They are both rolling about on the floor, with fists flying and Albert Steptoe still has his pants and underpants around his ankles. Other guests are coming out now to see what is happening and they are falling about laughing. The Pope is up on his feet and just manages to stick a hefty boot right between Albert Steptoe's legs and he curls up in a ball in agony on the drive way. By now the boss is outside as well and she is just stood there with eyes wide and her mouth gaping open. "Oh my God," she announces aloud, looking at me and Elvis in absolute hysterics. "Don't just stand there," she shouts at us, "go and sort them out!"

Now like all these parties, it usually ends for me with everything going black. I remember I'm leaning on some girl's shoulders being led to God knows where because I was in no fit state to care. Vaguely, I think it's Debbie Harry leading me along the landing after coming out the lift, and I can recall other guests coming out of their rooms complaining about the noise we were making. I was offering drunkenly to fight all of them but thankfully Debbie Harry dragged me into the room. I am now laid on the bed in total darkness and the room is spinning. It spins even more when the room is dark, and someone is pulling off my clothes. First my shirt is off and then my jeans and underpants are being ripped off and I can feel someone sucking on me like crazy. By this time, I have become accustomed to the darkness, and Debbie Harry is going for broke, sucking on me like a vacuum pump before mounting me and riding me like a Derby winner. Now being totally pissed and out of the game, she could have banged me until the cows come home and my knob would still have been as hard as rock. No matter how hard she rode me, nothing was happening for me and I just laid there being bounced up and down on the bed. All I could hear was Debbie Harry having the time of her life on top me. I have absolutely no idea how long this went on for, but things must have settled down eventually and I woke up some hours later feeling as randy as a bull. I just climbed aboard the body next to me and we were banging away. I must have had her in every conceivable position across that bed but I was still too drunk to finish myself off so we just kept at it and started rolling around the bed. Then suddenly there's a thud, like someone has fallen out the bed and I know it can't be the girl who is under me. Then a scream goes up as this body hits the floor. By this time, I'm confused and wondering what is going on so I drunkenly lean out the bed and put on the bedside lamp and there standing in all her naked glory is Debbie Harry staring down at me and looking like she is about to explode. I look at the other girl who is in bed with me. It's the hotel maid and she too is pissed up to the eye balls. I'm still trying to get my bearings and working out how I ended up in bed with both of them and banging them both in my drunken night time jolly.

But this time the party was just getting started and Debbie Harry was probably sobering up, probably concluding from the scene in front of her that ours was not going to be a match made in heaven. She launched herself onto the bed in a wild frenzy and started lashing out at me, screaming abuse like a wild banshee at the top her voice. Then she's off the bed and glasses and bottles are flying around the room, crashing and smashing against walls. Me and this hotel maid are still starkers in the bed and holding up pillows to protect ourselves from the barrage. "You dirty two timing bastard!" she is screaming at me. "And you! You! Fucking tramp!!" she screams at the maid. "Where did you come from?"

I was wondering that myself at this stage as I dived out of bed during a break in the bottle and glass fire and tried to calm her down and stop her from wrecking the room even more than she had already done.

We end up struggling around the room with Debbie Harry still screaming and we fall onto the bed. Now the three of us are rolling about on this bed and then suddenly the main light goes on and there standing in the doorway in their hotel bathrobes are Elvis, Alvin Stardust and the Pope. All three of us just freeze in mid-struggle on the bed then, just as you think it can't get any worse, the boss squeezes her head through and she's fuming.

"I expected better of you Terry!" she shouts at me, "and just look at this room!"

Elvis and Alvin Stardust have big silent grins on their faces and they bolt back to their rooms. The Pope just stares down in disapproval and shakes his head. "You disgusting little sod, isn't one enough for you? You'll be seeing the knob doctor soon the way you put it about."

The Pope disappeared to leave the boss scowling down at us. "If I hear another peep from this room, the lot of you will be out on your ear. Now get this room cleaned up and you," she said, pointing at Debbie Harry, "this is the third time I have caught dropping your knickers. I warned you, so pack your bags first thing, YOU'RE SACKED!" Then she turned on me again. "Now get this cleaned up, and I'll talk to you in the morning!"

By now I had totally sobered up. "Right boss," I replied timidly and pulled some covers over me to regain some dignity.

The next morning having tidied up the room I went downstairs to have the boss read the riot act to me. I was docked fifty notes for the damage to room. By this time, Debbie Harry had vacated the premises in ignominy. I never bumped into Debbie Harry again but it seemed the boss forgave me, or maybe because she knew she would never get as good a Rod Stewart lookalike as me. I was a bit disappointed with Debbie Harry when I later discovered that she had been banging half the lookalike crew for months because I thought she just had the hots for me.

And wait for it, the last lookalike she had been caught banging was the Pope. What did that say about me? As

Elvis later confessed to me. "I thought you knew she was a bit of a bike, Terry?"

"Don't tell me you banged her as well?" I said looking at him.

Elvis just raised his eyebrows, "I think everyone did."

"I thought I was a special," I said with a disappointed swoon. That was twice my delusions of being special had been dashed. Once with Tina and now Debbie Harry. Aren't women fickle, eh? If this wasn't bad enough, there was worse to come.

"I hate to tell you this Terry," said Elvis, "but last night after that bust-up in the car park, I caught Debbie Harry pissed as newt behind the stage parting her legs for Albert Steptoe. So you got Albert Steptoe's sloppy seconds last night."

Nothing like being brought down to earth is there? I ask you, I played second fiddle after Albert bleedin' Steptoe! The crew never let me live it down for a year if I ever got a bit full of myself. I ask you, Albert bloody Steptoe.

CHAPTER TWELVE

Well it was another job well done, sort of. I chilled out for the day at the hotel, used the gym, the sauna and got mildly drunk around the indoor swimming pool. I was absolutely knackered and turned in early around 8pm and fell asleep on top of my bed. I woke in darkness with someone gently tapping on my door and the door slowly opened. The hotel maid popped her head around the door with a big smile. "You're off tomorrow," she said with a note of regret.

"I gotta get back to ship." I whispered back.

And she smiled suggestively, "I just wondered if I could get you anything?"

"You'll get me shot," I said back with a smile.

"Don't worry about your boss," she with wide grin, "she got a call and checked out in a hurry."

"Well," I said grinning back, "you had better come in. I'm sure I can find something for you to do."

The next morning, I was up with the larks, bags packed and a taxi waiting. The maid had disappeared in the early hours and I jumped in the taxi. You know, I spent two nights in bed with that maid and I didn't even know her name. Thinking about it, I couldn't remember the names of half the birds I spent the night with in those few years, whether at sea or at lookalike parties. I was young and who cares anyway? I certainly didn't.

So anyway, I'm back on the ship and looking forward to another trip to Sweden only to get some really bad news. I get called up to the bridge with other senior crew, and the captain tells us: "We've had a change of plans."

"We're not going to Sweden?" I said with a note of disappointment. Anyone who has been to Sweden and seen the blonde bombshells walking about, would have been disappointed as well. I had few throbbing hot Swedish birds in my address book I was looking forward to looking up. Alas it was not to be. "So where are we going captain?" I ventured to ask.

"Swinoujscie," answered the captain.

I had never heard of it and I had been about a bit. This place, Swinoujscie, had a Godforsaken ring about it. And I was not going to be disappointed.

"Never heard of it," I said back.

"It's in Poland, " the captain answered, and instantly a groan went around the gathered group. Now you have to remember this was the 1970s and Poland was still under the firm iron fist of the Soviet Union and was a communist country. I had been to China in 1970s and Russia. Believe me, they were not fun places to visit. Dull, grey and usually bloody rock-solid freezing in winter.

The navigation officer drew out the charts and he let out another groan, "I thought so. The bloody Baltic Sea and it's well below zero at this time of year."

"Sorry lads," the captain said, "I want to be underway at the next tide." And with that we were dismissed.

The Baltic Sea was a whole new ball game for me. I was used to bad weather and ice having been a trawlerman and I had been above the Arctic circle but as we entered the Baltic Sea we were soon slowed down by the ice and eventually came to a standstill. So we're stuck in the ice and waiting for the ice breaker escorts that were always on standby to keep the shipping lanes open. Once under way again and we are joined by a train of other ships steaming through the ice behind the breakers. It was a long slow passage I can tell you and all there was to look at was, ice, snow and freezing fog. Yes, I was depressed, the whole crew was, but wait for it, the worst was yet come. When we reached the port they would not let us in as priority was being given to other communist Eastern bloc shipping.

Now in freezing Baltic waters you cannot just let your anchor down and wait. You would simply get frozen-in and ship's hull would be crushed by the pack ice. You had to steam in circle behind the ice breakers and wait until you got called in to port. Well one day turned into two and two days turned into seven days until we had been steaming in a circle for two bloody weeks until we finally got called into port. I think I was going stir crazy and dizzy with all this circling for two weeks. Like the rest of the crew I was also gagging for a shag and planned to be down that gang plank like a ship's rat looking for Polish totty to sooth my urges.

But this story gets worse and as we tied up an army of Polish customs descended on the ship and proceeded to go over it like shite hawks looking for any possible contraband. So me and the boys are all shit, showered and shaved and ready to hit town and dressed up to the nines. We are all in the mess sat impatiently twiddling our thumbs waiting for the all clear to go ashore. After the customs shake down, this Polish bird comes marching into the crew's mess in this heavy long black leather coat with senior rank epaulettes on the shoulders. She is all stern-faced and very official and had something of the SS about her. I guessed she was likely Polish secret service. They went by the initials of SB, and I won't even try and pronounce what the initials stood for but I did seem to catch her eye and I was sure I got a slight smile of sorts so I smiled back. Behind that stern face, she was a young, good looking blonde woman. Because of the coat it was hard to gauge what type of body she had but if the face and the blonde hair was anything to go by, I guessed she was likely hot.

She sat down without being asked, and went into a well - rehearsed routine about what we could and couldn't do. Remember we are in a communist country now and you're not allowed to just go down the gang plank and go where you like.

"You take only ten pounds sterling, and no more," she told us in cold but perfect English. "There is no transport off the docks but official party buses will take you. You are allowed only eight-hour shore passes. You will be given identity cards before going ashore." And that was it. I lit a cigarette and she looked at me expectantly. In those days, communist fags might have been cheap but it was like smoking camel dung so I offered her an English cigarette. She smiled and took one. She lit it with her own lighter and stood up.

"I think I speak with you," she said to me. It sounded more like an order than a request. I looked at the crew and they looked at me and I followed her outside into the gangway and she closed the mess room door.

She started with most incredible smile and these perfect white teeth were sparkling at me. "You are of interest to me," she said almost clinically. "We could go somewhere if you would like."

I don't know whether it was the black leather overcoat she was wearing, but I was getting signals here. I could only imagine what was waiting for me under that coat. Weeks at sea and I was ready, waiting and gagging to empty my sack. "What do you have in mind?" I asked her slowly.

"I like your face,' she said. All her initial ferocity had seemingly had left her and a young gorgeous woman was now standing in front me instead.

"So you have plans?" I asked her as suggestively as I could manage.

"I am important here," she said, "we can go where we like."

"But I've got be back in eight hours haven't I?" I said, leaving the question hanging in the air.

She furrowed her brow and grinned, took another drag from her fag, threw it on the floor and stamped on it.

"I think we will go now," she said almost in a whisper, and I just followed her off the ship to an official-looking clapped-out car. The armed guards waiting on the quayside clicked their heels in salute as she passed before she got in the driving seat and opened the passenger side. I got in and she just looked at me and smiled. She took off her official hat, unpinned her hair and shook her head, allowing her blonde locks to fall around her face and her shoulders. She was absolutely bloody stunning. She crunched the old banger into gear and we drove off the docks.

We drove in silence for about five minutes. "Where are we going," I asked her.

"Not far," she answered. "I thought we go to my place for a drink maybe?" She gave me a quick glance with this cheeky smile. "This is a very quiet town. If you have

English money, I know somewhere we can get good vodka."

She took me to what passed for a bar and I handed over about three pounds sterling. Two minutes later she came back with a bottle of vodka and I remember not getting any change, not that I asked for any. We passed through two check points and she seemed important enough just to be waved through and saluted.

After about twenty minutes we arrived at this huge grey depressing-looking block of flats. It was thick snow outside and it had just started snowing again outside. She parked the car and as we got out, she took hold of my hand like we were long time sweethearts and we took this shabby dimly-lit lift up a couple floors. This lift moved at snail's pace and the next I knew I was being kissed by this Polish beauty. This was slightly surreal the more I thought about it. Here was I, in a lift in some God forsaken town in deepest Poland, being snogged by a communist secret service police officer who was getting more aroused and amorous by the minute, as was I. By the time that lift came to halt and the doors opened onto to this unlit landing, she is heaving and pressing on me like a hungry wolf. Still holding tightly onto my hand as if I would run away, she led me up this long open landing with a depressing view that looked over this small port town. It was like a scene on a Christmas card because I could see some coloured lights here and there adorning the streets. We went into her flat. It was very basic and I had seen better furniture in a British junk shop. Once inside there's this bloke sitting on the couch looking up at me. There are some sharp words exchanged in Polish between my new friend and this Polish bloke who was a massive looking animal. If this was an angry husband, the thought occurred to me that I could be traveling at a great speed of knots head first over the balcony at any moment. Instead, this bloke just got up, put his coat on, smiled at me, shook my hand as he passed me and left quietly closing the door behind him.

"Who was that?" I asked her.

"Just my brother, he's not good with his wife, and staying a few days," she said

"I don't want you throw him out in the cold," I said awkwardly.

"This my flat," she said at me, "I need my own life also. Don't worry about him. He will get a drunk with his worthless friends. All men are useless in Poland. All they do is get drunk on vodka."

So we both sat down and she cracked the vodka open. I got the fags out and in between the odd long kiss we just chatted in the half light.

"You look like that famous person," she said smiling, "You are not him are you?"

I started laughing. "You mean Rod Stewart?"

"Yes, yes," she replied now laughing herself, "Rod Stewart, Maggie May. I don't think you are the real him but look like."

"No I'm not the real Rod Stewart. I hope I don't disappoint you."

She slowly shook her head without taking her eyes off me, "No, not disappointed."

Now in those days, Poland was a bit of a closed country and for merchant seaman, it had a reputation as a place to be avoided as all communist countries were at the time. I was curious to know she knew about Rod Stewart.

"How come you know so much about Rod Stewart?" I asked her.

"I don't know that much," she answered. She got up and took some English magazines out of a drawer and opened one to reveal a centrefold picture of Rod.

I started to laugh. "You get these in Poland?"

"No," she said, laughing sarcastically. "I confiscate them. You are not allowed such things in Poland." Then she winked. "I sometimes confiscate for myself."

It was a really slow sedate night and we just drank, talked and occasionally kissed as the hours floated by. I looked at my watch and it was one o'clock in the morning, and outside snowflakes cascaded down past the windows. I felt slightly drunk and very cosy and this Polish beauty was by now as tipsy as I was. She cuddled into my shoulder on the couch, occasionally kissing and gently biting my neck.

"I have to go," I whispered into her ear, "my eight hours are almost up."

"Don't worry about that," she whispered back through a long oozing kiss, "I make rules here." She lifted her head and looked at me. "We go to bed now, and you make love to me a long time."

Well, I never heard it put as romantically as that and, to tell you truth, in that cute smoldering Polish accent I was ready for action. She slowly got up from the couch and without taking her eyes off me she led me into the bedroom and we both fell gently on the bed. Just as easily, she slowly undressed me, kissing me all over as she skilfully removed each piece of my clothing and we submerged between the covers. If there was one thing I remember about her, it was her porcelain brilliant white skin. It was so smooth, so soft and her body had a smell to it I would remember till the end of my days. Of all the girls

I have known - and I have known many - this Polish girl
would follow me in my thoughts for many years.
I have to admit, it was one of the most hauntingly
memorable nights of my life. I seemed to have everything
that night.
Come the next morning and it was 10 o'clock when I woke
up. She was not in the bed and when I got up she was not
in the flat either. I looked around but she was gone. By
the time I got dressed I waited around for another half an
hour but she did not return. I made myself a hot cup of
coffee as it was freezing outside and the snow was still
pouring down. I had no idea where I was or how to get
back to the ship. About ten minutes later and there was a
knock at the flat door. It was a military-looking police
officer with a folding stock Kalashnikov hanging from his
shoulder standing outside. "Come," was the only word he
said and I followed him downstairs to a waiting car. It was
all very worrying and I was getting a little spooked. The
soldier opened the door for me and I climbed in the back.
The car door slammed shut and I was driven through the
snow. I couldn't see a thing outside with the blinding
snow pouring down and I had no idea where I was being
taken. After twenty minutes the car stopped and the door
was again opened for me. I was standing at the foot of the
ship's gang plank. I looked around half expecting to see
my mysterious Polish beauty but through the snow
pouring down I could see no one. I climbed the gang plank
and the car drove off. We stayed in port three more days,
and I was hoping every day my Polish princess would turn
up but much to my disappointment, she never did.
So the day came and we cast off forward, cast off aft and
we slowly pulled away from the quay side. By this time I
had given up hope of seeing her one last time. We must

have been about fifty metres away from the dockside when this official car pulled up and the lone figure of my mystery Polish girl climbed out of the car. She stood very still, just looking at me as I looked back at her. She gently smiled and waved to me and I waved back and the ship pulled away more. We both just stood staring at each other without moving and I'm sure I could see tears rolling down her face. I felt strange too. She waved one last time and I waved back and then distance faded us both to nothing, and suddenly her figure disappeared in the snow storm

For many days I never spoke with anyone. The Polish girl preyed on my mind day and night. I don't know what it was but I couldn't get her out of my thoughts for many months and would often dream about her. I suppose it might have been that I was taken by intensity and mystery of the moment. They often say there is one moment of love in every body's life that you never ever forget. I think that one night in Poland with that beautiful girl, was my magic moment. I still often think of her, even to this day.

THE END

Scallywag Books